Assessment Program

VISIONS

Basic Language and Literacy

Caroline Linse

Jane Yedlin

THOMSON

HEINLE

Australia • Canada • Mexico • Singapore • United Kingdom • United States

VISIONS BASIC ASSESSMENT PROGRAM
Caroline Linse and Jane Yedlin

Publisher: *Phyllis Dobbins*

Director of Development: *Anita Raducanu*

Senior Developmental Editor and Contributor: *Jill Korey O'Sullivan*

Developmental Editor: *Tania Maundrell-Brown*

Associate Developmental Editor: *Yeny Kim*

Associate Developmental Editor: *Kasia Zagorski*

Editorial Assistant: *Audra Longert*

Production Supervisor: *Mike Burggren*

Marketing Manager: *Jim McDonough*

Manufacturing Manager: *Marcia Locke*

Director, ELL Training and Development: *Evelyn Nelson*

Photography Manager: *Sheri Blaney*

Production Editor: *Samantha Ross*

Development: *Dan Greenberg*

Design and Production: *Publicom, Inc.*

Cover Designer: *Studio Montage*

Printer: *Globus Printing Company*

Printed in the United States of America
1 2 3 4 5 6 7 8 9 10   08   07   06   05   04   03

For more information contact Heinle, 25 Thomson Place, Boston, Massachusetts 02210 USA, or you can visit our Internet site at http://www.heinle.com

ISBN: 0-8384-5753-3

Contents

Credits

Photography

Corbis: p. 44 (© Casa Productions/Corbis), p.56 *B:11* (© Jose Luis Pelaez, Inc./Corbis), p.56 *B:14* (© Jim Zuckerman/ Corbis), p.58 (© Baldev/Corbis Sygma), p.62 (© Corbis Kipa), p. 72 (© Paul Velasco; Gallo Images/Corbis).

Getty Images Royalty Free: 2 *t* (© PhotoDisc/GettyImages), p.2 *C:12* (© PhotoDisc/GettyImages), p.13 *C:46* (© Eyewire/ PhotoDisc), p. 22 (© PhotoDisc/GettyImages), p. 69 (© PhotoDisc/GettyImages).

Getty Images Creative: p. 5 *t* (© Dick Luria/Taxi/GettyImages), p. 8 *r* (© Larry Bray/Taxi/GettyImages), p. 24 *B:13* (© Dick Luria/Taxi/GettyImages), p. 26 (© Dick Luria/Taxi/ GettyImages), p. 50 (© John Kelly/Stone/GettyImages), p. 52 *B:12* (© Larry Bray/Taxi/GettyImages).

Index Stock Photography: p. 2 *C:14* (© Aneal Vohra/Index Stock Imagery), p. 5 *K:48* (© Philip Wegener-Kantor/Index Stock Imagery), p. 8 *c* (© Bonnie Kamin/Index Stock Imagery), p. 12 *b* (© Benelux Press/Index Stock Imagery), p. 34 (© Wallace Garrison/Index Stock Imagery), p. 36 *t* (© JeffPerkell/ Index Stock Imagery), p. 36 *B:11* (© AnealVohra/Index Stock Imagery), p. 36 *B:15* (© James Lemass/Index Stock Imagery), p. 40 *B:20* (© Harvey Schwartz/Index Stock Imagery).

PictureQuest: p. 5 *K:50* (© Tony Freeman/PhotoEdit/ PictureQuest), p. 56 t (© Andersen-Ross/Brand X Pictures/PictureQuest), p. 69 b (© Andersen-Ross/ Brand X Pictures/ PictureQuest).

Any images not appearing here are acknowledged in the *Visions Basic Student Edition*.

Introduction and Overview

The *Visions Basic* Assessment Program was designed to ensure standards-based accountability for teachers and students alike. It begins with a Diagnostic Test to assess what students already know and to target students' needs in specific skill areas. Students take a quiz at the end of the preliminary Chapters A–D and at the end of each chapter for Chapters 1–10. The Assessment Program ensures ongoing as well as summative evaluation with the Mid-Book and End-of-Book Exams. Portfolio Assessment is also taken into account to measure the students' overall progress.

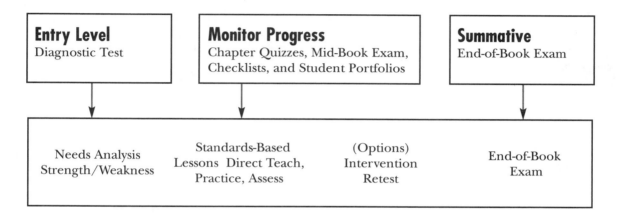

ExamView® is a CD-ROM assessment instrument that allows teachers to create and customize their *Visions Basic* Assessment Program. The Chapter Quizzes, Mid-Book Exam, and End-of-Book Exam can be customized by adding, deleting, editing, or rearranging questions from the test bank of standards-based assessment items. *ExamView*® also allows teachers to create and/or customize tests for the purpose of retesting after intervention.

Entry Level Placement

Heinle recognizes that English Language Learners usually take a placement test such as the *Language Assessment Scales* (LAS), the *California English Language Development Test* (CELDT), the *IDEA Proficiency Test* (IPT), or the Woodcock Muñoz. Heinle provides correlations to these placement tests so teachers know where to place students in the *Visions* program. (Contact your local Heinle/Thomson Learning Sales Representative for more information about these correlations.)

The *Visions* Program
- *Visions Basic:* Pre-literacy to beginning
- *Visions A:* Beginning
- *Visions B:* Intermediate
- *Visions C:* Advanced

Assessment Reference Chart

The reference chart below provides an overview of the assessment instruments, page numbers, and purpose of the assessment tools in the *Visions Basic* Assessment Program.

	Name	Pages	Purpose of Assessment
Entry Level	**Diagnostic Test**	1–8	To enable teachers to ascertain students' skills in listening and phonemic awareness, vocabulary, grammar, reading, and writing, and to do a Needs Analysis in order to target specific instructional needs.
Monitor Progress	**Chapter Quiz A–D**	9–18	To monitor students' literacy skills in listening, vocabulary, reading, writing, speaking, and decoding.
	Chapter Quizzes	19–38, 47–66	To monitor students' on-going progress toward meeting strategies and standards in listening, vocabulary, grammar, reading, and writing at the end of each chapter. There are 10 Chapter Quizzes.
	Mid-Book Exam	39–46	To monitor students' on-going progress toward meeting strategies and standards in listening, vocabulary, grammar, reading, writing, speaking, and spelling as taught throughout the first five chapters of the book.
	Student Resources Checklists	79–88	To promote student responsibility in meeting the standards. Students self-assess their strengths and weaknesses for purposes of reteaching if necessary.
Summative	**End-of-Book Exam**	67–74	To measure students' achievement and mastery in meeting the standards in listening, vocabulary, grammar, reading, writing, speaking, and spelling as taught throughout the book.
Monitor Progress	**Peer Editing** Checklist	81	To collaboratively involve students in giving and gaining feedback on their progress toward meeting the standards in writing.
	Active Listening Checklist	85	To collaboratively involve students in giving and gaining feedback on their progress in the area of listening and speaking during oral presentations.
	Reading Fluency	Activity Book and TRB, pp. 125–135	To check students' progress in learning to read silently and aloud with expression, and to adjust their reading rates according to the purpose of their reading.
	Teacher Resources Charts and Rubrics	xiii–xx	To evaluate students' overall performance using a fixed measurement scale and a list of criteria taken from formal and informal outcomes. These rubrics should be part of each student's permanent record.
	Portfolio Assessment	82	To involve students in self-reflection on their progress in meeting their learning goals. This on-going assessment is a collection of student work that exhibits the student's best efforts and progress.
	ExamView® CD-ROM	CD-ROM	To empower teachers to choose and customize test items to meet students' targeted needs; items chosen may be used to retest after intervention activities.

ENTRY LEVEL

DIAGNOSTIC TEST

The following subtests appear in the Diagnostic Test. These subtests may be taken all at once or at multiple diagnostic sessions.

Use the Teacher's Script on pp. xxiii–xxiv for sections A and B.

A. Phonemic Awareness Subtest This subtest assesses the learner's phonemic awareness.

B. Silent Letters Subtest This subtest assesses the learner's awareness of silent letters in English.

C. Vocabulary Subtest This subtest assesses the learner's vocabulary and ability to derive meaning from context. The ability to comprehend and read contextually is an indispensable skill, just as successful contextual reading requires an adequate vocabulary.

D. Concepts Subtest This subtest assesses the learner's ability to recognize basic vocabulary concepts.

E. Letter Recognition Subtest This subtest assesses the learner's ability to recognize upper and lowercase letters.

F. Syllables Subtest This subtest assesses the learner's ability to recognize basic syllable rules.

G. Word Analysis Subtest This subtest is made up of questions testing the learner's ability to recognize parts of words such as suffixes and prefixes.

H. Grammar Subtest This subtest evaluates skills that match the standards, taken from the Grammar Focus sections of *Visions Basic*.

I. Writing Conventions: Capitalization Subtest This subtest assesses capitalization skills by having students identify which words need a capital letter.

J. Writing Conventions: Punctuation Subtest This subtest assesses punctuation skills. Students must identify missing punctuation using a multiple-choice format.

K. Writing Conventions: Spelling Subtest This subtest assesses spelling skills. Students must identify mistakes using a multiple-choice format.

L. Reading Comprehension Subtest This subtest evaluates the learner's ability to answer questions about two silently-read passages. The learner's reading rate (fluency) may also be measured in addition to his/her understanding of the reading.

MONITORING PROGRESS

CHAPTER QUIZ A–D

For students who needed to complete Chapters A–D, there is a quiz at the end of this preliminary section. There are 75 multiple-choice questions and 20 writing items. The following subtests within the Chapter Quizzes reflect the skills that have been taught in the various sections of each chapter. A scoring guide has been included to ensure consistency and fairness.

Use the Teacher's Script on pp. xxiii–xxiv for section A.

A. **Letters and Sounds: Oral**   D. **Reading**

B. **Letters and Sounds: Written**   E. **Writing**

C. **Vocabulary**

In addition, there is a separate **Speaking Assessment** and a separate **Decoding Assessment.**

CHAPTER 1–10 QUIZZES

Each chapter has a four-page Quiz with 20 multiple-choice questions, writing items, and one writing prompt. The following subtests within the Chapter Quizzes reflect the skills that have been taught in the various sections of each chapter. A scoring guide has been included to ensure consistency and fairness.

Use the Teacher's Script on pp. xxiii–xxiv for section A.

A. **Listening**   D. **Reading**

B. **Vocabulary**   E. **Writing**

C. **Grammar**

SUMMATIVE EVALUATION

The *Visions Basic* Assessment Program includes two summative evaluations:

• **Mid-Book Exam** assesses skills covered in *Visions Basic,* Chapters 1–5.

• **End-of-Book Exam** assesses skills covered in *Visions Basic,* Chapters 1–10, with an emphasis on Chapters 6–10.

Both exams reflect the type and nature of testing done on standardized tests. They help prepare students to take language arts and English language-learner types of tests. The subtests within each Mid-Book Exam and End-of-Book Exam are the same as the Chapter subtests.

Use the Teacher's Script on pp. xxiii–xxiv for section A.

A. **Listening**   D. **Reading**

B. **Vocabulary**   E. **Writing**

C. **Grammar**

In addition, there is a separate **Speaking Assessment** and a separate **Spelling Assessment.**

VISIONS BASIC Assessment Program • Copyright © Heinle

TEACHER RESOURCES

ASSESSMENT MATERIALS

The following materials are provided for implementation of the quizzes and exams.

- **Answer Sheets** (pp. xi–xii) For ease-of-correction or for use when students cannot write directly on the testing materials.
- **Teacher Scripts** (pp. xxiii–xxiv) For use with the Listening sections of all testing materials.
- **Answer Key** (pp. 75–78) For correction of all testing materials.

TEACHER CHECKLISTS

The Teacher Resource checklists should be used to plan and evaluate instruction.
The following checklists are provided as reproducibles in this Assessment Program:

Teacher Checklists	Page
Diagnostic Test Results Chart	xiii
Individual Progress Chart: Formal	xiv
Individual Progress Chart: Authentic	xv
Rubric for Speaking Assessment	xvi
Assess Speaking Progress	xvii
Rubric for Writing Assessment	xviii
Assess Writing Progress	xix
Rubric for Oral Reading Fluency	xx

The *Rubric for Oral Reading Fluency* (p. xx) will help you assess the progress of your students during the Build Fluency sections of the student Activity Book.

STUDENT RESOURCES

PORTFOLIO ASSESSMENT

Introducing the portfolio Distribute a folder to each student in the class. Direct students to write their names on their portfolios and make a design, such as a coat-of-arms, that pictorially tells something about them. Write the word *portfolio* on the board and explain that the portfolio is a collection of their best work. At least one piece of their work from each chapter should go into their portfolio. Their portfolios should contain their best examples of the effort, progress, and achievements they have made throughout *Visions Basic.*

Student participation in selecting pieces Students should save all of the work they do in each unit in a work folder. At the end of each chapter, students will select their best work from this collection to add to their portfolio. Model the portfolio selection process by distributing the *Portfolio: Activity Rating and Reflection Sheet* (p. 82). Then, write on the board: "What is the piece or activity I liked the most?" Demonstrate removing the selected piece from their work folder and placing it in the portfolio.

Discuss the criteria for selecting pieces Review with the class the reasons for making a portfolio selection. Add their responses to a list on the board. Be sure to explain to students the following characteristics of a portfolio:

> • **It is continuous and on-going.** A portfolio contains samples of work that stretch over an entire marking period and can be accompanied by art, videotapes, and computer graphics.
> • **It provides for student reflection** about own work and learning.
> • **It contains a variety of different assessment tools** including student checklists.

Paulson, F.L. Paulson, P.R. and Meyer, CA. (1991, February). "What Makes a Portfolio a Portfolio?" *Educational Leadership,* pp. 60-63.

Portfolio: Activity Rating and Reflection Sheet Show students how to fill out the *Portfolio: Activity Rating and Reflection Sheet.* Have students work with a partner to share their work and discuss their responses before completing the sheet. When students have completed the sheet, have them attach it to the piece that they select to place in their portfolio.

Completing the portfolio process Explain where students should put their portfolios for storage until the next time they use them. Also explain where students should keep their work folders. The pieces of work gathered from the chapter that were not selected to include in the portfolio may be taken home.

STUDENT CHECKLISTS

Student Checklists are an integral part of the portfolio evaluation process. They provide feedback and a record of student progress in listening, speaking, reading, writing, and viewing. These checklists are provided as reproducibles in this Assessment Program:

READING FLUENCY

Student Practice Throughout *Visions Basic Activity Book,* students receive practice in the basic subskills of reading fluency. Each lesson is designed to cover and scaffold fluency instruction for English language learners. The subskills include rapid word recognition, echo read aloud, reading key phrases, word recognition of high-frequency words, chunking, scanning, and shared reading.

Teacher Notes Notes on the purpose of each Reading Fluency activity and how to implement it are found in the Teacher Resource Book, pp. 126-135.

The Reading Fluency Chart (Teacher Resource Book, p. 125) serves two assessment purposes. It serves as a record for:

- The number of words per minute a student reads aloud, and
- The number of words per minute a student reads silently.

After students have recorded their progress on their reading fluency charts, the students' grade level in reading fluency can be ascertained by referring to the rubric below.

Average rates for reading for students in Grades 2–12

Grade Equivalent	Standard Words Per Minute
2.5	121
3.5	135
4.5	149
5.5	163
6.5	177
7.5	191
8.5	205
9.5	219
10.5	233
11.5	247
12.5	261

Source: Carver (1990)
National Center for Education Statistics

VISIONS BASIC Assessment Program • Copyright © Heinle

Diagnostic Test Results Chart

Record students' scores for each section of the Diagnostic Test here.

Student Name	A. Phonemic Awareness 6 pts.	B. Silent Letters 8 pts.	C. Vocabulary 5 pts.	D. Concepts 4 pts.	E. Letter Recognition 5 pts.	F. Syllables 3 pts.	G. Word Analysis 4 pts.	H. Grammar 20 pts.	I, J, K. Writing Conventions 9 pts.	L. Reading 20 pts.	M. Writing 16 pts.	TOTAL 100 pts.
1.												
2.												
3.												
4.												
5.												
6.												
7.												
8.												
9.												
10.												
11.												
12.												
13.												
14.												
15.												

Individual Progress Chart: Formal Assessment

Student Name _____ Class _____

The purpose of this sheet is to record the student's progress and to use it as a basis for intervention and reteaching.

Note sections of tests where students are weak and target those areas as part of an intervention plan.

Formal Assessment

Record student's scores for each section of the quiz.
Write the number correct over the number of possible points for each section.

Chapters A–D Quiz		
Quiz Sections	**Score**	**Comments**
A. Letters and Sounds: Oral	/20	
B. Letters and Sounds: Written	/20	
C. Vocabulary	/20	
D. Reading	/20	
E. Writing	/20	
Speaking	/100	
Decoding	/100	

Chapters 1–10 Quizzes										
Quiz Sections	**1**	**2**	**3**	**4**	**5**	**6**	**7**	**8**	**9**	**10**
A. Listening	/20	/20	/20	/20	/20	/20	/20	/20	/20	/20
B. Vocabulary	/20	/20	/20	/20	/20	/20	/20	/20	/20	/20
C. Grammar	/20	/20	/20	/20	/20	/20	/20	/20	/20	/20
D. Reading	/20	/20	/20	/20	/20	/20	/20	/20	/20	/20
E. Writing	/20	/20	/20	/20	/20	/20	/20	/20	/20	/20

VISIONS BASIC Assessment Program • Copyright © Heinle

Individual Progress Chart: Authentic Assessment

Student Name _____ Class _____

Authentic Assessment
Record your observations of the student's strengths and needs.

Student Portfolio	Teacher Observation (language development, content, organization, other)
Chapters A–B	
Chapters C–D	
Chapters 1–2	
Chapters 3–4	
Chapters 5–6	
Chapters 7–8	
Chapters 9–10	

Interpersonal Skills	Teacher Observation (participation, cooperation, other)
Chapters A–B	
Chapters C–D	
Chapters 1–2	
Chapters 3–4	
Chapters 5–6	
Chapters 7–8	
Chapters 9–10	

Rubric for Speaking Assessment

Use this rubric to score students' speaking progress.

Also use it to score the Speaking Assessment for Chapters A–D Quiz, Mid-Book Exam, and End-of-Book Exam.

Each of the Speaking Assessments has 4 questions. Students earn a maximum of 25 points per question for a total of 100 points.

	5 points each element	3 points each element	1 point each element
Pronunciation/ Diction	• Student is easy to understand. Words and sounds are clear.	• Student makes minor errors in pronunciation.	• Student is very difficult to understand.
Fluency	• Student is comfortable speaking. • Student can effectively communicate in different situations.	• Student may show effort or timidity. • Student can generally communicate in most situations.	• Student is uncomfortable speaking. • Student cannot communicate effectively in all situations.
Word Choice	• Student uses exact words. • Student clearly varies speech based on purpose, audience, and subject matter.	• Student uses a lot of words to express simple meaning. • Student varies speech slightly based on purpose, audience, and subject matter.	• Student is limited to one- or two-word responses. • Student cannot vary speech based on purpose, audience, and subject matter.
Usage	• Student shows consistent control of grammar and structure.	• Student makes minor mistakes in grammar and structure	• Student makes major or frequent mistakes in grammar and structure that make speech difficult to understand.
Ideas/ Meaning	• Response matches question. • Student's ideas show thought. • Student supports and explains ideas clearly.	• Response almost matches question. • Student's ideas are generally meaningful.	• Response is weakly related to question. • Student's ideas are jumbled and disorganized.

VISIONS BASIC Assessment Program • Copyright © Heinle

VISIONS BASIC Assessment Program • Copyright © Heinle

Assess Speaking Progress

Assess oral skills in both formal and informal situations.
Keep track of each student's speaking progress.
Identify strengths and intervention areas by assessing each of the following elements of speaking.
Place a ✔ next to the elements that are developing well. Place an ✗ next to elements that need further attention.

Student Name _____ Class _____

Elements of Speaking	Date: Assessment:	Date: Assessment:	Date: Assessment:	Date: Assessment:	Date: Assessment:	Date: Assessment:
Pronunciation/Diction Speech is easy to understand. Words and sentences are clear.						
Fluency Student is comfortable speaking. Student can effectively communicate in different situations.						
Word Choice Student uses exact words. Word choice is appropriate to purpose, audience, and subject matter.						
Usage Grammar and usage are consistently controlled.						
Ideas/Meaning Responses match questions. Ideas show thought and are clearly explained.						

Rubric for Writing Assessment

Use this rubric to score students' writing assignments.
Also use it to score students' paragraph in the Writing section of the Chapter Quizzes and the Mid-Book and End-of-Book Exams.

The rubric is based on a perfect score of 10 points.

Elements of Good Writing	Points	Description
Ideas	2 points	• Ideas are developed. • Ideas are supported and explained.
Organization	1 point	• Ideas are ordered logically. • Organization is appropriate for topic.
Voice	1 point	• Writer engages the reader. • Writing sounds original. • Writer expresses individuality. • Writing is appropriate to the audience.
Sentence Fluency	1 point	• Writing stays focused. • Writing seems complete. • Writing is meaningful.
Word Choice	1 point	• Writer uses exact words to clarify and enhance meaning. • Writer uses language effectively.
Conventions	2 points	• Punctuation and capitalization are appropriate. • Spelling errors are few or none. • Grammar and usage are consistently appropriate. • Words, phrases, and sentence structures are used correctly and effectively.
Presentation	2 points	• Penmanship is pleasing. • Margins and spacing are appropriate. • Devices (headings, bullets, numbers, etc.) clarify and organize information.

VISIONS BASIC Assessment Program • Copyright © Heinle

Assess Writing Progress

Keep track of each student's writing progress.
Identify strengths and intervention areas by assessing each of the following elements of writing.
Place a ✔ next to the elements that are developing well. Place an **X** next to elements that need further attention.

Student Name _____ Class _____

Elements of Writing	Date: Sample:	Date: Sample:	Date: Sample:	Date: Sample:	Date: Sample:	Date: Sample:
Ideas Ideas are developed. Ideas are supported and explained.						
Organization Ideas are ordered logically. Organization is appropriate to topic.						
Voice Writer engages the reader Writing sounds original. Writing expresses individuality. Writing is appropriate to the audience.						
Sentence Fluency Writing stays focused. Writing seems complete. Writing is meaningful.						
Word Choice Writer uses exact words to clarify and enhance meaning. Writer uses language effectively.						
Conventions Punctuation, and capitalization are accurate. Spelling is accurate. Words, phrases, and sentence structure are used correctly and effectively.						
Presentation Penmanship is pleasing. Formatting is appropriate. Organizational devices (paragraphs, headings, bullets, etc.) are used appropriately.						

Rubric for Oral Reading Fluency

Use this rubric to score students' oral reading progress.

Points	Description of Oral Reading Fluency
4	Reads primarily in large, meaningful phrase groups. Although some regressions, repetitions, and deviations from text may be present, these do not detract from the overall structure of the reading. Preservation of syntax is consistent. Some or most of the reading is read with expressive interpretation.
3	Reads primarily in three- or four-word phrase groups. Some smaller groupings may be present. However, the majority of phrasing seems appropriate and preserves the syntax of the reading. Little or no expressive interpretation is present.
2	Reads primarily in two-word phrases with some three- or four-word groupings. Some word-by-word reading may be present. Word groupings may seem awkward and unrelated to the larger context of the sentence or passage.
1	Reads primarily word by word. Occasional two-word or three-word phrases may occur, but these are infrequent and/or they do not preserve meaningful syntax.

*Adapted from the National Assessment of Educational Progress (NAEP) Scale for Assessing Oral Reading Fluency

Student Name _____ Date _____

Answer Sheet

For Diagnostic Test, Chapters A–D Quiz, Mid-Book Exam, and End-of-Book Exam

_____ Diagnostic Test   _____ Mid-Book Exam
_____ Chapters A–D Quiz   _____ End-of-Book Exam

Fill in the circles of the correct answers. Erase mistakes well.

1. Ⓐ Ⓑ Ⓒ Ⓓ	26. Ⓐ Ⓑ Ⓒ Ⓓ	51. Ⓐ Ⓑ Ⓒ Ⓓ
2. Ⓐ Ⓑ Ⓒ Ⓓ	27. Ⓐ Ⓑ Ⓒ Ⓓ	52. Ⓐ Ⓑ Ⓒ Ⓓ
3. Ⓐ Ⓑ Ⓒ Ⓓ	28. Ⓐ Ⓑ Ⓒ Ⓓ	53. Ⓐ Ⓑ Ⓒ Ⓓ
4. Ⓐ Ⓑ Ⓒ Ⓓ	29. Ⓐ Ⓑ Ⓒ Ⓓ	54. Ⓐ Ⓑ Ⓒ Ⓓ
5. Ⓐ Ⓑ Ⓒ Ⓓ	30. Ⓐ Ⓑ Ⓒ Ⓓ	55. Ⓐ Ⓑ Ⓒ Ⓓ
6. Ⓐ Ⓑ Ⓒ Ⓓ	31. Ⓐ Ⓑ Ⓒ Ⓓ	56. Ⓐ Ⓑ Ⓒ Ⓓ
7. Ⓐ Ⓑ Ⓒ Ⓓ	32. Ⓐ Ⓑ Ⓒ Ⓓ	57. Ⓐ Ⓑ Ⓒ Ⓓ
8. Ⓐ Ⓑ Ⓒ Ⓓ	33. Ⓐ Ⓑ Ⓒ Ⓓ	58. Ⓐ Ⓑ Ⓒ Ⓓ
9. Ⓐ Ⓑ Ⓒ Ⓓ	34. Ⓐ Ⓑ Ⓒ Ⓓ	59. Ⓐ Ⓑ Ⓒ Ⓓ
10. Ⓐ Ⓑ Ⓒ Ⓓ	35. Ⓐ Ⓑ Ⓒ Ⓓ	60. Ⓐ Ⓑ Ⓒ Ⓓ
11. Ⓐ Ⓑ Ⓒ Ⓓ	36. Ⓐ Ⓑ Ⓒ Ⓓ	61. Ⓐ Ⓑ Ⓒ Ⓓ
12. Ⓐ Ⓑ Ⓒ Ⓓ	37. Ⓐ Ⓑ Ⓒ Ⓓ	62. Ⓐ Ⓑ Ⓒ Ⓓ
13. Ⓐ Ⓑ Ⓒ Ⓓ	38. Ⓐ Ⓑ Ⓒ Ⓓ	63. Ⓐ Ⓑ Ⓒ Ⓓ
14. Ⓐ Ⓑ Ⓒ Ⓓ	39. Ⓐ Ⓑ Ⓒ Ⓓ	64. Ⓐ Ⓑ Ⓒ Ⓓ
15. Ⓐ Ⓑ Ⓒ Ⓓ	40. Ⓐ Ⓑ Ⓒ Ⓓ	65. Ⓐ Ⓑ Ⓒ Ⓓ
16. Ⓐ Ⓑ Ⓒ Ⓓ	41. Ⓐ Ⓑ Ⓒ Ⓓ	66. Ⓐ Ⓑ Ⓒ Ⓓ
17. Ⓐ Ⓑ Ⓒ Ⓓ	42. Ⓐ Ⓑ Ⓒ Ⓓ	67. Ⓐ Ⓑ Ⓒ Ⓓ
18. Ⓐ Ⓑ Ⓒ Ⓓ	43. Ⓐ Ⓑ Ⓒ Ⓓ	68. Ⓐ Ⓑ Ⓒ Ⓓ
19. Ⓐ Ⓑ Ⓒ Ⓓ	44. Ⓐ Ⓑ Ⓒ Ⓓ	69. Ⓐ Ⓑ Ⓒ Ⓓ
20. Ⓐ Ⓑ Ⓒ Ⓓ	45. Ⓐ Ⓑ Ⓒ Ⓓ	70. Ⓐ Ⓑ Ⓒ Ⓓ
21. Ⓐ Ⓑ Ⓒ Ⓓ	46. Ⓐ Ⓑ Ⓒ Ⓓ	71. Ⓐ Ⓑ Ⓒ Ⓓ
22. Ⓐ Ⓑ Ⓒ Ⓓ	47. Ⓐ Ⓑ Ⓒ Ⓓ	72. Ⓐ Ⓑ Ⓒ Ⓓ
23. Ⓐ Ⓑ Ⓒ Ⓓ	48. Ⓐ Ⓑ Ⓒ Ⓓ	73. Ⓐ Ⓑ Ⓒ Ⓓ
24. Ⓐ Ⓑ Ⓒ Ⓓ	49. Ⓐ Ⓑ Ⓒ Ⓓ	74. Ⓐ Ⓑ Ⓒ Ⓓ
25. Ⓐ Ⓑ Ⓒ Ⓓ	50. Ⓐ Ⓑ Ⓒ Ⓓ	75. Ⓐ Ⓑ Ⓒ Ⓓ

Student Name _____ Date _____

Answer Sheet

For Chapters 1–10 Quizzes

Chapter _____ Quiz

Fill in the circles of the correct answers. Erase mistakes well.

1.	Ⓐ	Ⓑ	Ⓒ	Ⓓ		18.	Ⓐ	Ⓑ	Ⓒ	Ⓓ
2.	Ⓐ	Ⓑ	Ⓒ	Ⓓ		19.	Ⓐ	Ⓑ	Ⓒ	Ⓓ
3.	Ⓐ	Ⓑ	Ⓒ	Ⓓ		20.	Ⓐ	Ⓑ	Ⓒ	Ⓓ
4.	Ⓐ	Ⓑ	Ⓒ	Ⓓ		21.	Ⓐ	Ⓑ	Ⓒ	Ⓓ
5.	Ⓐ	Ⓑ	Ⓒ	Ⓓ		22.	Ⓐ	Ⓑ	Ⓒ	Ⓓ
6.	Ⓐ	Ⓑ	Ⓒ	Ⓓ		23.	Ⓐ	Ⓑ	Ⓒ	Ⓓ
7.	Ⓐ	Ⓑ	Ⓒ	Ⓓ		24.	Ⓐ	Ⓑ	Ⓒ	Ⓓ
8.	Ⓐ	Ⓑ	Ⓒ	Ⓓ		25.	Ⓐ	Ⓑ	Ⓒ	Ⓓ
9.	Ⓐ	Ⓑ	Ⓒ	Ⓓ		26.	Ⓐ	Ⓑ	Ⓒ	Ⓓ
10.	Ⓐ	Ⓑ	Ⓒ	Ⓓ		27.	Ⓐ	Ⓑ	Ⓒ	Ⓓ
11.	Ⓐ	Ⓑ	Ⓒ	Ⓓ		28.	Ⓐ	Ⓑ	Ⓒ	Ⓓ
12.	Ⓐ	Ⓑ	Ⓒ	Ⓓ		29.	Ⓐ	Ⓑ	Ⓒ	Ⓓ
13.	Ⓐ	Ⓑ	Ⓒ	Ⓓ		30.	Ⓐ	Ⓑ	Ⓒ	Ⓓ
14.	Ⓐ	Ⓑ	Ⓒ	Ⓓ		31.	Ⓐ	Ⓑ	Ⓒ	Ⓓ
15.	Ⓐ	Ⓑ	Ⓒ	Ⓓ		32.	Ⓐ	Ⓑ	Ⓒ	Ⓓ
16.	Ⓐ	Ⓑ	Ⓒ	Ⓓ		33.	Ⓐ	Ⓑ	Ⓒ	Ⓓ
17.	Ⓐ	Ⓑ	Ⓒ	Ⓓ		34.	Ⓐ	Ⓑ	Ⓒ	Ⓓ

VISIONS BASIC Assessment Program • Copyright © Heinle

Teacher Script

The following is the script to be read by the teacher for all listening sections of the tests and quizzes.

Diagnostic Test

A. Phonemic Awareness

➤ **Listen to the word. Choose the word you hear.**

Example: meet

1. say
2. rip
3. bet
4. noise
5. tube
6. pin

B. Silent Letters

➤ **Listen to the word. Look at the word. Choose the letter that is silent.**

Example: date

7. knees
8. hour
9. write
10. listen

Quiz: Chapters A–D

A. Letters and Sounds

➤ **Listen to the letter sound. Which letter has the sound?**

Example: m [pronounce the m sound]

1. d [pronounce the d sound]
2. h [pronounce the h sound]
3. a [pronounce the short a sound]
4. e [pronounce the e sound]
5. r [pronounce the r sound]

➤ **Listen to the letter sound. Which picture has the beginning sound?**

Example: a [pronounce the short a sound, as in apple]

6. p [pronounce the p sound, as in pencil]
7. i [pronounce the short i sound, as in insect]
8. w [pronounce the w sound, as in woman]
9. m [pronounce the m sound, as in map]
10. s [pronounce the s sound, as in sun]

➤ **Listen to the word. Which word has the same beginning sound?**

Example: ring

11. apple
12. queen
13. orange
14. nose
15. hand

➤**Listen to the word. Which word has the same short vowel sound?**

Example: cat

16. dot
17. six
18. yes
19. hug
20. bed

Quiz: Chapter 1

A. Listening

➤ **Listen to the word. Find the word in the sentence. Mark the word.**

Example: *You hear:* pen.

1. month
2. mouse
3. stapler
4. date
5. parent

➤ **Listen to the word. Which word has the same sound?**

Example: Which word has the same short i sound?
You hear: lips.

6. Which word has the same short o sound? top
7. Which word has the same short a sound? hat
8. Which word has the same short e sound? yes
9. Which word has the same short u sound? bus
10. Which word has the same short i sound? hit

Quiz: Chapter 2

A. Listening

➤ **Listen to the sentence. Choose the missing word.**

Example: We have a cat and a dog.

1. My grandfather is very tall.
2. Victor has straight blond hair.
3. Your brother's dog is very cute.
4. The green and yellow bird is from Chile.
5. Your grandmother is not tall.

➤ **Listen to the word. Which word has the same sound?**

Example: Which word has the same long i sound?
You hear: like.

6. Which word has the same long o sound? note
7. Which word has the same long a sound? face
8. Which word has the same long u sound? tube
9. Which word has the same long i sound? like
10. Which word has the same long o sound? nose

Quiz: Chapter 3

A. Listening

➤ **Listen to the word. Find the word in the sentence. Mark the word.**

Example: *You hear:* play.

1. soccer
2. paint
3. baseball
4. meet
5. read

➤ **Listen to the sentence. Choose the missing word.**

Example: I meet my friends on Saturday morning.

6. I sometimes play the guitar.
7. I often go to work after school.
8. On Friday we always rent a video.
9. When you play baseball, you need a bat.
10. My sister plays the drums.

Quiz: Chapter 4

A. Listening

➤ **Listen to the sentence. Choose the missing word.**

Example: There is a sofa in the living room.

1. I take a shower in the bathroom.
2. There is pizza in the refrigerator.
3. You often listen to the radio.
4. There are three pillows on the bed.
5. There is a dog on the rug in the living room.

➤ **Listen to the word. Find the word in the sentence. Mark each word.**

Example: bedrooms

6. bathtub
7. armchair
8. backpack
9. classrooms
10. bookcase

Quiz: Chapter 5

A. Listening

➤ **Listen to the sentence. Write the missing word.**

Example: The train comes at three o'clock.
1. Oscar walks to the police station.
2. How do you get to the supermarket?
3. It is one thirty.
4. The restaurant is on Third Street.
5. The movie theater is near the park.

➤ **Listen to the word. Choose the missing letters.**

Example: *You hear:* shop.
6. chin
7. thank
8. ring
9. fish
10. where

Mid-Book Exam: Chapters 1–5

A. Listening

➤ **Listen to the word. Find the word in the sentence. Mark each word.**

Example: *You hear:* address.
1. beautiful
2. exercise
3. refrigerator
4. hospital
5. handsome

➤ **Listen to the word. Choose the word that rhymes with the word.**

Example: *You hear:* bug.
6. white
7. speak
8. late
9. ring
10. cap

Quiz: Chapter 6

A. Listening

➤ **Listen to the sentence. Choose the missing word.**

Example: I eat breakfast every morning.
1. For lunch, we have spaghetti.
2. Do you need a napkin?
3. I need a fork and a knife.
4. Every day, Phan eats cereal for breakfast.
5. I put some soup in a bowl.

➤ **Listen to the word. Find the word in the sentence. Mark each word.**

Example: *You hear:* chicken.
6. tomatoes
7. beans
8. pizza
9. toast
10. sandwiches

Quiz: Chapter 7

A. Listening

➤ **Listen to the sentence. Choose the missing word.**

Example: I pay with a check.
1. The customer is in the store.
2. We use an ATM card to get money.
3. What is the name of the salesperson?
4. I buy clothes with a credit card.
5. Do you have a quarter?

Example: repaint
6. rewrite
7. review
8. retell
9. recount
10. repay

Quiz: Chapter 8

A. Listening

➤ **Listen to the word. Find the word in the sentence. Mark each word.**

Example: *You hear:* doctor.
1. chef
2. cashier
3. artist
4. waiter
5. clerk

➤ **Listen to the word. Choose the best answer.**

Example: *You hear:* painter.
6. gardener
7. manager
8. singer
9. dancer
10. child care worker

Quiz: Chapter 9

A. Listening

➤ **Listen to the sentence. Choose the missing word.**

Example: We see the fireworks in the sky.
1. After dinner, Sid opened a box of chocolates.
2. There is stuffing inside the turkey.
3. The parade on Fourth of July is beautiful.
4. On Valentine's Day, Steve got a card from Jan.
5. Pink and yellow flowers grow in the garden.

➤ **Listen to the word. Which word has the same sound?**

Example: spill
6. start
7. skip
8. speak
9. study
10. spell

Quiz: Chapter 10

A. Listening

➤ **Listen to the word. Find the word in the sentence. Mark each word.**

Example: excited
1. yawns
2. blush
3. smiles
4. sad
5. shout

➤ **Listen to the word. Which word rhymes with the word?**

Example: rose
6. fat
7. hear
8. fish
9. run
10. when

End-of-Book Exam: Chapters 6–10

A. Listening

➤ **Listen to the word. Find the word in the sentence. Mark the word.**

Example: *You hear:* breakfast.
1. nickel
2. check
3. chef
4. flag
5. scared

➤ **Listen to the sentence. Choose the missing word.**

Example: reread
6. rice
7. painter
8. think
9. tomatoes
10. rewrite

Name _____ Date _____

Diagnostic Test

A. Phonemic Awareness (6 points: 1 point each)

➤ **Listen to the word your teacher says. Choose the word you hear.**

Example: *You hear:* meet.

Ⓐ meet
Ⓑ met
Ⓒ mat
Ⓓ mate

1. Ⓐ see
   Ⓑ so
   Ⓒ say
   Ⓓ saw

2. Ⓐ rap
   Ⓑ ripe
   Ⓒ rip
   Ⓓ rope

3. Ⓐ bit
   Ⓑ bat
   Ⓒ beat
   Ⓓ bet

4. Ⓐ rose
   Ⓑ nose
   Ⓒ notes
   Ⓓ none

5. Ⓐ tube
   Ⓑ rule
   Ⓒ tub
   Ⓓ rub

6. Ⓐ pin
   Ⓑ pit
   Ⓒ bin
   Ⓓ pine

B. Silent Letters (8 points: 2 points each)

➤ **Listen to the word your teacher says. Look at the word. Choose the letter that is silent.**

Example: *You hear:* date.
Which letter is silent?

Ⓐ d
Ⓑ a
Ⓒ t
Ⓓ e

7. knees
   Ⓐ k
   Ⓑ n
   Ⓒ e
   Ⓓ s

8. hour
   Ⓐ h
   Ⓑ o
   Ⓒ u
   Ⓓ r

9. write
   Ⓐ w
   Ⓑ r
   Ⓒ i
   Ⓓ t

10. listen
    Ⓐ n
    Ⓑ t
    Ⓒ e
    Ⓓ l

Name _____   Date _____

Diagnostic Test *(continued)*

C. Vocabulary (5 points: 1 point each)

➤ **Match the picture to the word.**

Example:

Ⓐ square
Ⓑ circle
Ⓒ heart
Ⓓ triangle

11.

Ⓐ mother
Ⓑ family
Ⓒ boy
Ⓓ dog

12.

Ⓐ orange
Ⓑ school
Ⓒ sandwich
Ⓓ apple

13.

Ⓐ bedroom
Ⓑ computer
Ⓒ pencil
Ⓓ cap

14.

Ⓐ table
Ⓑ car
Ⓒ post office
Ⓓ pencil

15.

Ⓐ surprised
Ⓑ sad
Ⓒ angry
Ⓓ embarrassed

D. Concepts (4 points: 1 point each)

➤ **Choose the correct answer.**

Example:

Ⓐ 1:00
Ⓑ 6:15
Ⓒ 9:30
Ⓓ 12:00

16. What number is missing?
3, 4, ___, 6, 7, 8, 9
Ⓐ 1
Ⓑ 5
Ⓒ 0
Ⓓ 2

17. What time is it?

Ⓐ 9:00
Ⓑ 5:30
Ⓒ 2:10
Ⓓ 1:45

18. Which day is missing?
Sunday, Monday, ___,
Wednesday,
Ⓐ March
Ⓑ Tuesday
Ⓒ Thursday
Ⓓ Saturday

19. How much money is this?

Ⓐ $6
Ⓑ 5¢
Ⓒ 6¢
Ⓓ 11¢

VISIONS BASIC Assessment Program • Copyright © Heinle

Name _____ Date _____

Diagnostic Test *(continued)*

E. Letter Recognition
(5 points: 1 point each)

➤ Match the uppercase letter to the lowercase letter.

Example: M
- Ⓐ w
- **Ⓑ** m
- Ⓒ n
- Ⓓ r

20. P
- Ⓐ d
- Ⓑ q
- Ⓒ p
- Ⓓ o

21. F
- Ⓐ l
- Ⓑ h
- Ⓒ f
- Ⓓ t

22. A
- Ⓐ u
- Ⓑ e
- Ⓒ o
- Ⓓ a

23. I
- Ⓐ l
- Ⓑ p
- Ⓒ i
- Ⓓ r

24. Q
- Ⓐ d
- Ⓑ p
- Ⓒ g
- Ⓓ q

F. Syllables (3 points: 1 point each)

➤ Divide each word into syllables.

Example: keyboard
- Ⓐ ke • yboard
- Ⓑ ke • ybo • ard
- **Ⓒ** key • board
- Ⓓ keybo • ard

25. football
- Ⓐ fo • otball
- Ⓑ foo • tball
- Ⓒ foot • ball
- Ⓓ footb • all

26. dimple
- Ⓐ di • mp • le
- Ⓑ dim • pl • e
- Ⓒ dim • ple
- Ⓓ dimp • le

27. computer
- Ⓐ co • mp • u • ter
- Ⓑ comp • u • ter
- Ⓒ comp • uter
- Ⓓ com • put • er

G. Word Analysis (4 points: 1 point each)

➤ Choose the meaning of the underlined word.

Example: Maria <u>dislikes</u> tomatoes.
- Ⓐ likes a lot
- Ⓑ sounds like
- **Ⓒ** does not like
- Ⓓ is like

28. The girl looks <u>unhappy</u>.
- Ⓐ joyful
- Ⓑ not happy
- Ⓒ very angry
- Ⓓ very happy

Name _____ Date _____

Diagnostic Test *(continued)*

29. You must <u>rewrite</u> this paper.
Ⓐ write again
Ⓑ not write
Ⓒ right away
Ⓓ give away

30. She works in a <u>windowless</u> office.
Ⓐ with one window
Ⓑ with a lot of windows
Ⓒ with no windows
Ⓓ with eleven windows

31. Picasso is a famous <u>painter</u>.
Ⓐ to not paint
Ⓑ a color of paint
Ⓒ to paint again
Ⓓ a person who paints

H. Grammar (20 points: 2 points each)

➤ **Choose the missing word.**

Example: I ___ a good soccer player.
Ⓐ are
Ⓑ be
Ⓒ is
🅓 am

32. Are ___ a new student?
Ⓐ I
Ⓑ she
Ⓒ you
Ⓓ they

33. I ___ to school every day.
Ⓐ go
Ⓑ going
Ⓒ goes
Ⓓ gone

34. Miguel ___ to play baseball.
Ⓐ liking
Ⓑ like
Ⓒ do like
Ⓓ likes

35. We ___ to Florida every year.
Ⓐ fli
Ⓑ fly
Ⓒ flies
Ⓓ flying

36. Please ___ do that!
Ⓐ stop
Ⓑ no
Ⓒ don't
Ⓓ you not

37. Right now, Rosa ___ to music on the radio.
Ⓐ listen
Ⓑ are listening
Ⓒ is listening
Ⓓ is listen

38. You ___ your lunch to school every day.
Ⓐ bring
Ⓑ brings
Ⓒ is bring
Ⓓ bringing

39. Yesterday, Ana ___ on the phone.
Ⓐ talk
Ⓑ talks
Ⓒ talked
Ⓓ is talked

40. Last night we ___ a strange noise.
Ⓐ hear
Ⓑ hears
Ⓒ heared
Ⓓ heard

41. They ___ finish their work in class.
Ⓐ aren't
Ⓑ didn't
Ⓒ isn't
Ⓓ not

VISIONS BASIC Assessment Program • Copyright © Heinle

Diagnostic Test *(continued)*

I. Writing Conventions: Capitalization (3 points: 1 point each)

➤ **Choose the word that should have a capital letter.**

Example: We live in the state of texas.
- Ⓐ Live
- Ⓑ State
- Ⓒ Of
- ⬤ Texas

42. our teacher is very nice.
- Ⓐ Our
- Ⓑ Teacher
- Ⓒ Very
- Ⓓ Nice

43. We will go to our new school on monday.
- Ⓐ Will
- Ⓑ New
- Ⓒ School
- Ⓓ Monday

44. Our new teacher's name is mr. Garcia.
- Ⓐ New
- Ⓑ Teacher's
- Ⓒ Name
- Ⓓ Mr.

J. Writing Conventions: Punctuation (3 points: 1 point each)

➤ **Choose the missing punctuation.**

Example: Ouch ___ That hurts!
- Ⓐ .
- Ⓑ ?
- Ⓒ ,
- ⬤ !

45. Do you have a pencil___
- Ⓐ .
- Ⓑ ?
- Ⓒ ,
- Ⓓ !

46. Please shut the door___
- Ⓐ .
- Ⓑ ?
- Ⓒ ,
- Ⓓ "

47. The colors are red ___ yellow, and blue.
- Ⓐ .
- Ⓑ ?
- Ⓒ ,
- Ⓓ !

K. Writing Conventions: Spelling (3 points: 1 point each)

➤ **Choose the correct spelling.**

Example:

- Ⓐ fomly
- Ⓑ famly
- ⬤ family
- Ⓓ familie

48.
- Ⓐ kichen
- Ⓑ kitchn
- Ⓒ kitchin
- Ⓓ kitchen

49.
- Ⓐ nickl
- Ⓑ nikel
- Ⓒ nickel
- Ⓓ nickul

50.
- Ⓐ parad
- Ⓑ perade
- Ⓒ parade
- Ⓓ prad

Diagnostic Test *(continued)*

L. Reading Comprehension (20 points: 2 points each)

➤ **Read and answer the questions.**

Reading 1

Things to Do

Lea wants to go to a party today. First she has some things to do. It is 10 a.m. The party starts at 4 p.m. Do you think she can do everything on her list before the party?

---

51. Who is this story about?
  Ⓐ Joe
  Ⓑ Miguel
  Ⓒ Lea
  Ⓓ the dog

52. Where does Lea want to go?
  Ⓐ to the park
  Ⓑ to a party
  Ⓒ for a walk
  Ⓓ before 4 p.m.

53. What time does the party start?
  Ⓐ 10:00 in the morning
  Ⓑ 10:00 at night
  Ⓒ 4:00 in the morning
  Ⓓ 4:00 in the afternoon

54. What will Lea clean?
  Ⓐ the park
  Ⓑ her brother
  Ⓒ her room
  Ⓓ her clothes

55. What is the second thing that Lea must do?
  Ⓐ clean her room
  Ⓑ wash her clothes
  Ⓒ bring her brother to the park
  Ⓓ take the dog for a walk

Things to Do

1. clean my room
2. wash my clothes
3. bring my brother to the park
4. take the dog for a walk

Name _____   Date _____

Diagnostic Test *(continued)*

<u>Reading 2</u>

> ### A Class Trip
>
> "I have something to tell you, class," the teacher announced. "On Monday, we will take a trip to the city. We will leave at 7 a.m. We will travel on a big bus. We will spend the day at the Museum of History. Then we will have dinner at a restaurant. We will return to the school at 6 p.m."
>
> "Yea!" the students cheered. "A class trip to the city will be fun!"

56. What is this story about?
- Ⓐ the Museum of History
- Ⓑ a class trip
- Ⓒ dinner at a restaurant
- Ⓓ a big bus

57. Who does the teacher tell about the class trip?
- Ⓐ the teachers
- Ⓑ the parents
- Ⓒ the students
- Ⓓ the restaurant

58. When is the class trip?
- Ⓐ Monday
- Ⓑ Tuesday
- Ⓒ Wednesday
- Ⓓ Friday

59. What will the students visit on their class trip?
- Ⓐ a football game
- Ⓑ a museum
- Ⓒ a bus
- Ⓓ a small town

60. What time will the students return to the school?
- Ⓐ 7:00 in the morning
- Ⓑ 7:00 at night
- Ⓒ 6:00 in the morning
- Ⓓ 6:00 at night

Name _____ Date _____

Diagnostic Test (continued)

M. The Writing Process (16 points: #61, 1 point; #62, 5 points; #63, 10 points)

61. Step 1

➤ Look at each picture. Choose one picture to write about. Circle the picture.

62. Step 2

➤ Write notes about the picture.

63. Step 3

➤ Write a paragraph to describe the picture.

_____

_____

_____

_____

_____

_____

_____

VISIONS BASIC Assessment Program • Copyright © Heinle

Name _____ Date _____

Quiz: Chapters A–D

A. Letters and Sounds: Oral
(20 points: 1 point each)

➤ **Listen to the letter sound. Which letter has the sound?**

Example: *You hear:* m.
- Ⓐ b
- Ⓒ s
- Ⓑ m
- Ⓓ t

1. Ⓐ c Ⓒ d
Ⓑ f Ⓓ n

2. Ⓐ h Ⓒ r
Ⓑ j Ⓓ v

3. Ⓐ e Ⓒ c
Ⓑ o Ⓓ a

4. Ⓐ a Ⓒ i
Ⓑ e Ⓓ f

5. Ⓐ r Ⓒ f
Ⓑ s Ⓓ g

➤ **Listen to the letter sound. Which picture has the beginning sound?**

Example: *You hear:* a.
Ⓐ Ⓒ
Ⓑ   Ⓓ

6. Ⓐ Ⓒ
Ⓑ Ⓓ

7. Ⓐ Ⓒ
Ⓑ Ⓓ

8. Ⓐ Ⓒ
Ⓑ Ⓓ

9. Ⓐ Ⓒ
Ⓑ Ⓓ

10. Ⓐ Ⓒ
Ⓑ Ⓓ

9

Name _____   Date _____

Quiz: Chapters A–D *(continued)*

➤ **Listen to the word. Which word has the same beginning sound?**

Example: *You hear:* ring.
- Ⓐ orange
- Ⓑ pizza
- ⬤ rose
- Ⓓ tag

11.
- Ⓐ ant
- Ⓑ key
- Ⓒ window
- Ⓓ zipper

12.
- Ⓐ hat
- Ⓑ quarter
- Ⓒ nose
- Ⓓ pen

13.
- Ⓐ office
- Ⓑ up
- Ⓒ egg
- Ⓓ insect

14.
- Ⓐ bag
- Ⓑ newspaper
- Ⓒ gate
- Ⓓ sun

15.
- Ⓐ jeans
- Ⓑ fan
- Ⓒ gate
- Ⓓ hat

➤ **Listen to the word. Which word has the same short vowel sound?**

Example: *You hear:* cat.
- Ⓐ cot
- Ⓑ yes
- Ⓒ up
- ⬤ bag

16.
- Ⓐ fan
- Ⓑ pen
- Ⓒ jog
- Ⓓ cup

17.
- Ⓐ hug
- Ⓑ map
- Ⓒ egg
- Ⓓ lip

18.
- Ⓐ in
- Ⓑ dog
- Ⓒ wet
- Ⓓ six

19.
- Ⓐ cup
- Ⓑ jog
- Ⓒ hat
- Ⓓ insect

20.
- Ⓐ ten
- Ⓑ six
- Ⓒ van
- Ⓓ on

VISIONS BASIC Assessment Program • Copyright © Heinle

Name _____   Date _____

Quiz: Chapters A–D *(continued)*

B. Letters and Sounds: Written
(20 points: 1 point each)

➤ **Match the uppercase letter to the lowercase letter.**

Example: M
- Ⓐ s
- Ⓑ a
- Ⓒ n
- Ⓓ m

21. f
- Ⓐ F
- Ⓑ w
- Ⓒ J
- Ⓓ v

22. L
- Ⓐ l
- Ⓑ k
- Ⓒ p
- Ⓓ U

23. e
- Ⓐ Q
- Ⓑ H
- Ⓒ L
- Ⓓ E

24. q
- Ⓐ M
- Ⓑ Q
- Ⓒ f
- Ⓓ P

25. J
- Ⓐ i
- Ⓑ j
- Ⓒ e
- Ⓓ F

➤ **Look at the picture. What is the first letter of the word that the picture shows?**

Example:

- Ⓐ b
- Ⓑ j
- Ⓒ s
- Ⓓ r

26.
- Ⓐ f
- Ⓑ r
- Ⓒ e
- Ⓓ n

27.
- Ⓐ q
- Ⓑ g
- Ⓒ j
- Ⓓ m

28.
- Ⓐ y
- Ⓑ k
- Ⓒ m
- Ⓓ n

29.
- Ⓐ o
- Ⓑ u
- Ⓒ e
- Ⓓ a

30.
- Ⓐ p
- Ⓑ q
- Ⓒ d
- Ⓓ b

Quiz: Chapters A–D *(continued)*

➤ **Which word has the same sound?**

Example: Which word has the same *a* sound as *bag?*

Ⓐ sat
Ⓑ name
Ⓒ gate
Ⓓ library

31. Which word has the same *e* sound as *yes?*
Ⓐ bed
Ⓑ leaf
Ⓒ table
Ⓓ video

32. Which word has the same *u* sound as *hug?*
Ⓐ computer
Ⓑ quarter
Ⓒ blue
Ⓓ cup

33. Which word has the same *i* sound as *six?*
Ⓐ library
Ⓑ lip
Ⓒ stripe
Ⓓ hair

34. Which word has the same *o* sound as *pot?*
Ⓐ yellow
Ⓑ dot
Ⓒ nose
Ⓓ you

35. Which word has the same *a* sound as *apple?*
Ⓐ gate
Ⓑ fan
Ⓒ chair
Ⓓ name

➤ **What's the missing letter?**

Example:

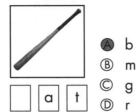

| a | t |

Ⓐ b
Ⓑ m
Ⓒ g
Ⓓ r

36.

| a | n |

Ⓐ m
Ⓑ c
Ⓒ f
Ⓓ v

37.

| b | e | |

Ⓐ w
Ⓑ d
Ⓒ b
Ⓓ i

38.

| p | | t |

Ⓐ o
Ⓑ a
Ⓒ e
Ⓓ i

39.

| | o | g |

Ⓐ d
Ⓑ b
Ⓒ f
Ⓓ l

40.

| h | | g |

Ⓐ i
Ⓑ e
Ⓒ u
Ⓓ o

VISIONS BASIC Assessment Program • Copyright © Heinle

Quiz: Chapters A–D (continued)

C. Vocabulary (20 points: 1 point each)

➤ **Which word matches the picture?**

Example:

ⓐ man
ⓑ board
ⓒ principal
🅓 girl

41.

ⓐ eraser
ⓑ desk
ⓒ window
ⓓ office

42.

ⓐ nose
ⓑ lips
ⓒ arm
ⓓ leg

43.

ⓐ chair
ⓑ clock
ⓒ outside
ⓓ cheek

44.

ⓐ office
ⓑ clock
ⓒ computer
ⓓ desk

45.

ⓐ jacket
ⓑ pencil
ⓒ book
ⓓ backpack

46.

ⓐ library
ⓑ sneakers
ⓒ stars
ⓓ sweater

47.

ⓐ nose
ⓑ second
ⓒ mouth
ⓓ chin

48.

ⓐ eraser
ⓑ first
ⓒ face
ⓓ flag

49.

ⓐ jeans
ⓑ pencil
ⓒ jacket
ⓓ skirt

50.

ⓐ stairs
ⓑ library
ⓒ window
ⓓ hall

Name _____ Date _____

Quiz: Chapters A–D *(continued)*

➤ **What's the missing word?**

Example: Hi. My _____ is Mrs. Rana.
- Ⓐ what's
- Ⓑ hello
- ⬤ name
- Ⓓ leg

51. Where is the _____ pen?
- Ⓐ man
- Ⓑ is
- Ⓒ red
- Ⓓ that

52. My name _____ Emilio.
- Ⓐ is
- Ⓑ your
- Ⓒ in
- Ⓓ me

53. Is this your _____?
- Ⓐ outside
- Ⓑ yours
- Ⓒ from
- Ⓓ backpack

54. The book is _____ the chair.
- Ⓐ your
- Ⓑ under
- Ⓒ hello
- Ⓓ what

55. The elevator is next to the _____.
- Ⓐ left
- Ⓑ chin
- Ⓒ stairs
- Ⓓ first

56. How old _____ you?
- Ⓐ is
- Ⓑ from
- Ⓒ there
- Ⓓ are

57. Where's the nurse's _____?
- Ⓐ office
- Ⓑ period
- Ⓒ outside
- Ⓓ question

58. The _____ is on the first floor.
- Ⓐ second
- Ⓑ head
- Ⓒ gym
- Ⓓ across

59. My backpack is _____.
- Ⓐ fingers
- Ⓑ stairs
- Ⓒ nose
- Ⓓ green

60. His eyes are _____.
- Ⓐ board
- Ⓑ these
- Ⓒ brown
- Ⓓ numbers

VISIONS BASIC Assessment Program • Copyright © Heinle

Quiz: Chapters A–D *(continued)*

D. Reading (20 points: 1 point each for 61–70; 2 points each for 71–75)

➤ **What's the missing word?**

Example: Hi. _____ name is Mr. Green.
Ⓐ Ana
Ⓑ Hello
Ⓒ My
Ⓓ You

61. What is _____ name?
Ⓐ you
Ⓑ your
Ⓒ yours
Ⓓ me

62. I'm _____ Vietnam.
Ⓐ for
Ⓑ from
Ⓒ is
Ⓓ mine

63. How many stars _____ on the flag?
Ⓐ has
Ⓑ are
Ⓒ you
Ⓓ he

64. _____ is my green pen?
Ⓐ What's
Ⓑ The
Ⓒ Where
Ⓓ My

65. _____ pencil is black.
Ⓐ My
Ⓑ Where
Ⓒ Me
Ⓓ Mine

66. My name is Irina. I _____ a student.
Ⓐ are
Ⓑ is
Ⓒ has
Ⓓ am

67. There are 15 boys _____ your class.
Ⓐ on
Ⓑ in
Ⓒ is
Ⓓ this

68. _____ are eight teachers in my school.
Ⓐ This
Ⓑ The
Ⓒ That
Ⓓ There

69. How _____ are you?
Ⓐ old
Ⓑ years
Ⓒ woman
Ⓓ me

70. The cafeteria is _____ to the gym.
Ⓐ next
Ⓑ on
Ⓒ no
Ⓓ yes

Name _____ Date _____

Quiz: Chapters A–D (continued)

A New Student

Excuse me. My name is Irina Rostov. I'm a student in this school. Where is Room 209?

Good morning, Irina. My name is Mr. Escobar. I'm your teacher. Room 209 is my classroom. Go up the stairs. It's on the right, next to the library.

➤ **Read and choose the best answer to each question.**
Example: Who is Irina?
- Ⓐ He is a teacher.
- Ⓑ She's a student.
- Ⓒ He's a student.
- Ⓓ She's from Mexico.

71. Where is Irina?
- Ⓐ She's a student.
- Ⓑ She's in her house.
- Ⓒ She's in Mexico.
- Ⓓ She's in school.

72. Who is Mr. Escobar?
- Ⓐ He's a teacher.
- Ⓑ He's a student.
- Ⓒ He's from Russia.
- Ⓓ She's a teacher.

73. What is Mr. Escobar's classroom?
- Ⓐ the library
- Ⓑ Room 109
- Ⓒ Room 209
- Ⓓ the bathroom

74. Where is the classroom?
- Ⓐ next to Room 209
- Ⓑ down the stairs on the right
- Ⓒ up the stairs on the left
- Ⓓ up the stairs on the right

75. What is next to the classroom?
- Ⓐ the school
- Ⓑ the library
- Ⓒ Room 209
- Ⓓ the hall

VISIONS BASIC Assessment Program • Copyright © Heinle

Name _____ Date _____

Quiz: Chapters A–D *(continued)*

E. Writing (20 points: 1 point each)

➤ **Copy the letters.**

Example: A A A A A A

76. R __ __ __ __ __

77. n __ __ __ __ __

78. L __ __ __ __ __

79. J __ __ __ __ __

80. K __ __ __ __ __

➤ **Copy the words.**

Example: hello h e l l o

81. name __ __ __ __

82. arm __ __ __

83. mine __ __ __ __

84. there __ __ __ __ __

85. head __ __ __ __

➤ **Write words to complete the sentences.**

Example: I'm _from_ Mexico.

86. Hello. My _____ is Lisa.

87. _____ morning, Lisa.

88. I'm Mrs. Garcia. I'm your _____.

89. Where are you _____, Lisa?

90. I'm from _____, Mrs. Garcia.

91. Where is my _____, Mrs. Garcia?

92. Your classroom is on the _____ floor.

93. The classroom has an American _____.

94. The flag has red and _____ stripes.

95. The main office is on the first _____.

Speaking Assessment (100 points: 25 points each)

See Rubric for Speaking Assessment, p. xvi

This Speaking Assessment provides an opportunity to assess students' speaking skills. To administer the test, have students open to the indicated page in their student book. Ask them the questions. Students are graded based on the Rubric for Speaking Assessment on p. xvi of this Assessment Guide.

1. Look at the picture on page 22. Who is Mrs. Garcia? What's the first girl's name? What's the second girl's name? Where is Ana from? What's your name? Where are you from?

2. Look at the picture on page 23. What color is the flag? How many stars are there? How many stripes are there? What color is your backpack? What color is your pencil?

3. Look at pages 28 and 29. Who is wearing jeans? Who is wearing sneakers? What color is the girl's hat? What color is your shirt (sweater)? What color is your hair? What color are your eyes?

4. Look at page 49. What's the nurse's name? What's the gym teacher's name? What is your gym teacher's name? Where is the gym in your school? Where is the main office?

✂ —

Decoding Assessment (100 points: 5 points each)

This Decoding Assessment provides students with a list of words that test letter sound decoding skills. Students are expected to know both vowel and consonant sounds and to display mastery of how letter sounds blend to form words. To administer the test, point to each word on the list and have the student read it aloud.

1. man
2. bag
3. jog
4. lip
5. wet
6. pot
7. cup
8. gate
9. mop
10. yes

11. six
12. red
13. gas
14. desk
15. dot
16. dog
17. hand
18. girl
19. hug
20. king

VISIONS BASIC Assessment Program • Copyright © Heinle

Name _____ Date _____

Quiz: Chapter 1

A. Listening (20 points: 2 points each)

➤ **Listen to the word. Find the word in the sentence. Mark the word.**

Example: *You hear:* pen
Do you need a pen or a pencil?
Ⓐ Ⓑ Ⓒ   ⬤(D)

1. March is the third month of the year.
   Ⓐ   Ⓑ Ⓒ   Ⓓ

2. The computer has a new mouse.
   Ⓐ   Ⓑ   Ⓒ   Ⓓ

3. The stapler is on the table.
   Ⓐ   Ⓑ   Ⓒ   Ⓓ

4. The date today is January 20.
   Ⓐ   Ⓑ   Ⓒ   Ⓓ

5. Your parent is your mother or father.
   Ⓐ   Ⓑ   Ⓒ   Ⓓ

➤ **Listen to the word. Which word has the same sound?**

Example: Which word has the same short *i* sound? *You hear:* lips.
Ⓐ birth
Ⓑ mine
⬤ hit
Ⓓ right

6. Which word has the same short *o* sound?
   Ⓐ hot
   Ⓑ old
   Ⓒ telephone
   Ⓓ hello

7. Which word has the same short *a* sound?
   Ⓐ May
   Ⓑ name
   Ⓒ day
   Ⓓ map

8. Which word has the same short *e* sound?
   Ⓐ need
   Ⓑ please
   Ⓒ ten
   Ⓓ code

9. Which word has the same short *u* sound?
   Ⓐ you
   Ⓑ under
   Ⓒ student
   Ⓓ Thursday

10. Which word has the same short *i* sound?
    Ⓐ printer
    Ⓑ machine
    Ⓒ Friday
    Ⓓ ninth

Name _____ Date _____

Quiz: Chapter 1 *(continued)*

B. Vocabulary (20 points: 2 points each)

➤ **Find the word that names the picture.**

Example:

Ⓐ parent
Ⓑ teacher
Ⓒ guardian
Ⓓ secretary *(filled)*

11.

Ⓐ printer
Ⓑ copy machine
Ⓒ calendar
Ⓓ stapler

12.

Ⓐ computer
Ⓑ keyboard
Ⓒ mouse
Ⓓ form

13.

Ⓐ printer
Ⓑ office
Ⓒ keyboard
Ⓓ mouse

14.

Ⓐ copy machine
Ⓑ calendar
Ⓒ month
Ⓓ Sunday

15.

Ⓐ screen
Ⓑ keyboard
Ⓒ mouse
Ⓓ telephone

➤ **Find the word that best completes the sentence.**

Example: Today's _____ is March 4.
Ⓐ calendar
Ⓑ month
Ⓒ date *(filled)*
Ⓓ day

16. Please fill in this student information _____.
Ⓐ form
Ⓑ screen
Ⓒ guardian
Ⓓ pencil

17. _____ is March third.
Ⓐ October
Ⓑ year
Ⓒ week
Ⓓ Wednesday

18. February is the _____ month of the year.
Ⓐ fourteenth
Ⓑ only
Ⓒ second
Ⓓ first

19. What is your _____ number?
Ⓐ telephone
Ⓑ week
Ⓒ zip code
Ⓓ date

20. The school _____ is in the main office.
Ⓐ guardian
Ⓑ street
Ⓒ secretary
Ⓓ father

VISIONS BASIC Assessment Program • Copyright © Heinle

Name _____ Date _____

Quiz: Chapter 1 *(continued)*

C. Grammar (20 points: 2 points each)

➤ **Find the word that best completes the sentence.**

Example: This is _____ pencil.
Ⓐ mine
Ⓑ you
Ⓒ my
Ⓓ I

21. _____ parents are from Mexico.
Ⓐ She
Ⓑ Her
Ⓒ He
Ⓓ They

22. _____ is in the cafeteria.
Ⓐ He
Ⓑ They
Ⓒ His
Ⓓ Her

23. _____ are from California.
Ⓐ Her
Ⓑ My
Ⓒ They
Ⓓ Their

24. _____ teacher is Mrs. Garcia.
Ⓐ You
Ⓑ Your
Ⓒ Hers
Ⓓ Him

25. _____ am a student.
Ⓐ We
Ⓑ I
Ⓒ My
Ⓓ Our

26. _____ class is in Room 206.
Ⓐ I
Ⓑ Our
Ⓒ We
Ⓓ You

27. _____ has four legs.
Ⓐ It
Ⓑ Her
Ⓒ Their
Ⓓ Them

28. _____ are in the library.
Ⓐ Her
Ⓑ His
Ⓒ Our
Ⓓ We

29. Nikolai is _____ first name.
Ⓐ it
Ⓑ you
Ⓒ my
Ⓓ mine

30. _____ are a good student.
Ⓐ Your
Ⓑ My
Ⓒ You
Ⓓ It

Name _____ Date _____

Quiz: Chapter 1 *(continued)*

D. Reading (20 points: 5 points each)

┌───┐
The Form

Esteban Cruz fills in a Student Information Form. Esteban's address is 262 Ninth Street, Coral Gables, Florida 33124. His telephone number is (305) 555–6213. Gloria Cruz and Eddie Cruz are Esteban's parents.
└───┘

➤ **Choose the best answer.**

Example: What is the name of the form?
Ⓐ Student Form
Ⓑ Address Form
Ⓒ Student Information Form
Ⓓ Information Form

31. What city does Esteban live in?
Ⓐ Coral Gables
Ⓑ Florida
Ⓒ Coral
Ⓓ Ninth Street

32. What is Esteban's zip code?
Ⓐ 262
Ⓑ 33124
Ⓒ (305)
Ⓓ 555-6213

33. What is Esteban's area code?
Ⓐ 262
Ⓑ 33124
Ⓒ (305)
Ⓓ 555-6212

34. What is the first name of Esteban's mother?
Ⓐ Esteban
Ⓑ Gloria
Ⓒ Coral
Ⓓ Cruz

E. Writing (20 points: 2 points each)

➤ **Fill in the form with information about you.**

STUDENT INFORMATION FORM

35. DATE _____

36. LAST NAME _____

37. FIRST NAME _____

38. ADDRESS _____

39. CITY _____

40. STATE _____

41. ZIP CODE _____

42. PHONE _____

43. DATE OF BIRTH _____

44. PARENT OR GUARDIAN _____

_____

VISIONS BASIC Assessment Program • Copyright © Heinle

Name _____ Date _____

Quiz: Chapter 2

A. Listening (20 points: 2 points each)

➤ **Listen to the sentence. Choose the missing word.**

Example: *You hear:* We have a cat and a dog.
We have a _____ and a dog.
Ⓐ fish
Ⓑ pet
Ⓒ cat
Ⓓ car

1. My _____ is very tall.
Ⓐ grandmother
Ⓑ grandfather
Ⓒ father
Ⓓ brother

2. Victor has straight _____ hair.
Ⓐ blond
Ⓑ brown
Ⓒ beautiful
Ⓓ black

3. Your brother's dog is very _____.
Ⓐ tall
Ⓑ cut
Ⓒ cute
Ⓓ short

4. The green and yellow _____ is from Chile.
Ⓐ pet
Ⓑ cat
Ⓒ bid
Ⓓ bird

5. Your grandmother is not _____.
Ⓐ thin
Ⓑ too
Ⓒ tall
Ⓓ tell

➤ **Listen to the word. Which word has the same sound?**

Example: *You hear:* like.
Which word has the same long *i* sound?
Ⓐ thin
Ⓑ white
Ⓒ kit
Ⓓ sister

6. Which word has the same long *o* sound?
Ⓐ hot
Ⓑ hope
Ⓒ hop
Ⓓ not

7. Which word has the same long *a* sound?
Ⓐ made
Ⓑ mad
Ⓒ tall
Ⓓ am

8. Which word has the same long *u* sound?
Ⓐ tub
Ⓑ curly
Ⓒ cut
Ⓓ rule

9. Which word has the same long *i* sound?
Ⓐ nice
Ⓑ eight
Ⓒ rain
Ⓓ thin

10. Which word has the same long *o* sound?
Ⓐ brother
Ⓑ long
Ⓒ note
Ⓓ not

Name _____ Date _____

Quiz: Chapter 2 *(continued)*

B. Vocabulary (20 points: 2 points each)

➤ **Find the word that names the picture.**

Example:

- Ⓐ dog
- Ⓑ bird
- Ⓒ cat
- Ⓓ fish

11.

- Ⓐ blond
- Ⓑ brown
- Ⓒ blue
- Ⓓ black

12.

- Ⓐ heavy
- Ⓑ weight
- Ⓒ thin
- Ⓓ height

13.

- Ⓐ sister
- Ⓑ brother
- Ⓒ grandmother
- Ⓓ family

14.

- Ⓐ straight
- Ⓑ curly
- Ⓒ long
- Ⓓ blond

15.

- Ⓐ fish
- Ⓑ foot
- Ⓒ bird
- Ⓓ dog

➤ **Find the word that best completes the sentence.**

Example: My _____ has long hair.
- Ⓐ bird
- Ⓑ sister
- Ⓒ fish
- Ⓓ cute

16. His brother is very _____.
- Ⓐ wavy
- Ⓑ straight
- Ⓒ curly
- Ⓓ short

17. They have a _____ dog named Goldie.
- Ⓐ cute
- Ⓑ cat
- Ⓒ cut
- Ⓓ coat

18. My grandmother is _____.
- Ⓐ sister
- Ⓑ beautiful
- Ⓒ wavy
- Ⓓ straight

19. Your _____ is tall.
- Ⓐ fish
- Ⓑ hair
- Ⓒ short
- Ⓓ grandfather

20. I have _____ length hair.
- Ⓐ medium
- Ⓑ black
- Ⓒ red
- Ⓓ blond

VISIONS BASIC Assessment Program • Copyright © Heinle

Quiz: Chapter 2 *(continued)*

C. Grammar (20 points: 2 points each)

➤ **Find the word that best completes the sentence.**

Example: She _____ my friend.
Ⓐ am
Ⓑ is
Ⓒ are
Ⓓ be

21. I _____ from Mexico.
Ⓐ am
Ⓑ be
Ⓒ are
Ⓓ is

22. The cat _____ cute.
Ⓐ am
Ⓑ is
Ⓒ are
Ⓓ was

23. The chairs _____ very heavy.
Ⓐ are
Ⓑ be
Ⓒ am
Ⓓ was

24. Ana and Tina _____ sisters.
Ⓐ is
Ⓑ am
Ⓒ be
Ⓓ are

25. You _____ average height.
Ⓐ be
Ⓑ is
Ⓒ are
Ⓓ am

26. I _____ not a student.
Ⓐ be
Ⓑ am
Ⓒ is
Ⓓ are

27. Clara _____ not heavy.
Ⓐ am
Ⓑ be
Ⓒ are
Ⓓ is

28. We _____ in the library.
Ⓐ are
Ⓑ is
Ⓒ be
Ⓓ am

29. You _____ 14 years old.
Ⓐ am
Ⓑ are
Ⓒ is
Ⓓ be

30. My fish _____ blue and yellow.
Ⓐ am
Ⓑ be
Ⓒ does
Ⓓ is

Name _____ Date _____

Quiz: Chapter 2 *(continued)*

D. Reading (20 points: 5 points each)

> **My Grandmother**, *by Sylvia Wong*
>
> My grandmother is a
>   beautiful woman.
> Her eyes are brown and
>   small.
> She is average weight.
>   Her hair is wavy.
> She is nice and kind and tall.

➤ **Choose the best answer.**

Example: Who is the poem about?
Ⓐ a girl's grandfather
🅑 a girl's grandmother
Ⓒ a girl's mother
Ⓓ a girl's brother

31. What color are the grandmother's eyes?
Ⓐ blue
Ⓑ small
Ⓒ brown
Ⓓ black

32. What is the grandmother's hair like?
Ⓐ brown and curly
Ⓑ wavy
Ⓒ long and white
Ⓓ straight

33. What is the grandmother like?
Ⓐ She is heavy.
Ⓑ She is cute.
Ⓒ She has dimples.
Ⓓ She is beautiful and nice.

34. Who is the poem by?
Ⓐ Mary Ann Hoberman
Ⓑ Sylvia Hoberman
Ⓒ Sylvia Wong
Ⓓ Mary Wong

E. Writing (20 points: #35–44, 1 point each; #45, 10 points)

➤ **Describe a female family member. Write the words that best complete the sentences. Use the information in parentheses to help you.**

Describing a Family Member

My (**35.**) _____ is very

(**36.**) _____ .

Her eyes are (**37.**) _____ *(color)*.

They are not (**38.**) _____ .

She is (**39.**) _____ *(height)*.

She is not (**40.**) _____ .

She is (**41.**) _____ *(weight)*.

Her hair is (**42.**) _____ *(length)*,

(**43.**) _____ *(color)*, and

(**44.**) _____ .

45. Who is your good friend?

➤ **On a separate piece of paper, describe your good friend. Write a short paragraph.**

VISIONS BASIC Assessment Program • Copyright © Heinle

Name _____ Date _____

Quiz: Chapter 3

A. Listening (20 points: 2 points each)

➤ **Listen to the word. Find the word in the sentence. Mark the word.**

Example: *You hear:* play
Do you play an instrument?
Ⓐ Ⓑ ⬤Ⓒ Ⓓ

1. Sometimes, I play soccer with friends.
   Ⓐ   Ⓑ Ⓒ   Ⓓ

2. Do you have some green paint?
   Ⓐ   Ⓑ Ⓒ Ⓓ

3. I need a new baseball bat.
   Ⓐ   Ⓑ Ⓒ Ⓓ

4. After school, I usually meet my friends.
   Ⓐ   Ⓑ Ⓒ   Ⓓ

5. I read the newspaper in the morning.
   Ⓐ   Ⓑ   Ⓒ Ⓓ

➤ **Listen to the sentence. Choose the missing word.**

Example: *You hear:* I meet my friends on Saturday morning.
I meet my _____ on Saturday morning.
Ⓐ friends
Ⓑ swim
Ⓒ sport
Ⓓ usually

6. I sometimes play the _____.
   Ⓐ soccer
   Ⓑ friend
   Ⓒ work
   Ⓓ guitar

7. I often go to _____ after school.
   Ⓐ video
   Ⓑ work
   Ⓒ music
   Ⓓ play

8. On Friday, we always _____ a video.
   Ⓐ work
   Ⓑ dance
   Ⓒ write
   Ⓓ rent

9. When you play baseball, you need a _____.
   Ⓐ pain
   Ⓑ bat
   Ⓒ drums
   Ⓓ instrument

10. My sister plays the _____.
    Ⓐ paint
    Ⓑ soccer
    Ⓒ drums
    Ⓓ paint

Name _____ Date _____

Quiz: Chapter 3 *(continued)*

B. Vocabulary (20 points: 2 points each)

➤ **Find the word that names the picture.**

Example:

Ⓐ guitar
🅑 video
Ⓒ computer
Ⓓ soccer

11.

Ⓐ play
Ⓑ rent
Ⓒ swim
Ⓓ jog

12.

Ⓐ soccer
Ⓑ baseball
Ⓒ dance
Ⓓ exercise

13.

Ⓐ baseball
Ⓑ drums
Ⓒ guitar
Ⓓ write

14.

Ⓐ pen
Ⓑ paint
Ⓒ work
Ⓓ bat

15.

Ⓐ jog
Ⓑ swim
Ⓒ rent
Ⓓ write

➤ **Find the word that best completes the sentence.**

Example: I _____ to music every day.
Ⓐ play
Ⓑ rent
● listen
Ⓓ shop

16. Jen and Tran play _____.
Ⓐ an exercise
Ⓑ an instrument
Ⓒ a baseball
Ⓓ a pen

17. My friends usually _____ on Saturday.
Ⓐ shop
Ⓑ video
Ⓒ sport
Ⓓ sometimes

18. I usually rent a _____ on Thursday.
Ⓐ shop
Ⓑ baseball
Ⓒ video
Ⓓ work

19. Liz writes _____ every day.
Ⓐ e-mail
Ⓑ play
Ⓒ listen
Ⓓ drum

20. I _____ new friends at work.
Ⓐ video
Ⓑ shop
Ⓒ swim
Ⓓ meet

VISIONS BASIC Assessment Program • Copyright © Heinle

Quiz: Chapter 3 *(continued)*

C. Grammar (20 points: 2 points each)

➤ **Find the word that best completes the sentence.**

Example: The teacher _____ in the school.
- Ⓐ read
- Ⓑ work
- Ⓒ works
- Ⓓ play

21. I sometimes _____ baseball after school.
- Ⓐ read
- Ⓑ play
- Ⓒ plays
- Ⓓ reads

22. Andrei always _____ to music.
- Ⓐ listen
- Ⓑ listens
- Ⓒ play
- Ⓓ rent

23. On Wednesdays, I _____ in an office.
- Ⓐ work
- Ⓑ works
- Ⓒ rent
- Ⓓ rents

24. We _____ a new book every week.
- Ⓐ rent
- Ⓑ reads
- Ⓒ read
- Ⓓ red

25. Luis _____ the drums for his friends.
- Ⓐ jog
- Ⓑ swim
- Ⓒ play
- Ⓓ plays

26. You _____ the newspaper every morning.
- Ⓐ read
- Ⓑ reads
- Ⓒ play
- Ⓓ rents

27. Doug and Mike _____ on Tuesday.
- Ⓐ exercises
- Ⓑ plays
- Ⓒ exercise
- Ⓓ sometimes

28. Tia _____ after work.
- Ⓐ jog
- Ⓑ jogs
- Ⓒ rents
- Ⓓ meet

29. Paula and Meg _____ for a new skirt.
- Ⓐ shop
- Ⓑ shops
- Ⓒ read
- Ⓓ reads

30. I _____ every day.
- Ⓐ swims
- Ⓑ soccer
- Ⓒ jog
- Ⓓ works

Name _____ Date _____

Quiz: Chapter 3 *(continued)*

D. Reading (20 points: 5 points each)

After School

After school, Jorge meets his friend Jimmy. Sometimes they roller skate on the street. Sometimes they play music. Jorge plays the guitar and Jimmy plays the drums. Sometimes, Jorge and Jimmy play baseball. This is fun!

➤ **Choose the best answer.**

Example: Who is the story about?
Ⓐ school
Ⓑ Jorge's brother
Ⓒ Jorge and Jimmy
Ⓓ baseball

31. When do Jorge and Jimmy meet?
Ⓐ after school
Ⓑ before school
Ⓒ in school
Ⓓ in the morning

32. What do Jorge and Jimmy play?
Ⓐ soccer
Ⓑ dance
Ⓒ baseball and soccer
Ⓓ music and baseball

33. What instrument does Jorge play?
Ⓐ the drums
Ⓑ a baseball team
Ⓒ the guitar
Ⓓ roller skates

34. What sport do Jorge and Jimmy play?
Ⓐ music
Ⓑ the guitar
Ⓒ baseball
Ⓓ the drums

E. Writing (20 points: #35–44, 1 point each; #45, 10 points)

➤ **Write the words that best complete the sentences. Use the information in parentheses to help you.**

Favorites

My favorite sport is (**35.**) _____.

I play this sport with (**36.**) _____ *(who?).*

I (**37.**) _____ *(how often?)* play this sport (**38.**) _____ *(when?).*

I need (**39.**) _____ *(object)* to play this sport.

My favorite music is (**40.**) _____.

I like to listen to this music with (**41.**) _____ *(who?).*

I usually listen to this music (**42.**) _____ *(when?).*

My favorite instrument is (**43.**) _____.

(**44.**) I _____ play this instrument *(how often?).*

45. What activities do you do?

➤ **On a separate piece of paper, write a short paragraph about the activities you do. Say how often you do them and who you do them with.**

VISIONS BASIC Assessment Program • Copyright © Heinle

Quiz: Chapter 4

A. Listening (20 points: 2 points each)

➤ **Listen to the sentence. Choose the missing word.**

Example: *You hear:* There is a sofa in the living room.
There is a _____ in the living room.
- Ⓐ bookcase
- Ⓑ lamp
- ⬤ sofa
- Ⓓ table

1. I take a _____ in the bathroom.
- Ⓐ bathtub
- Ⓑ shower
- Ⓒ mirror
- Ⓓ sofa

2. There is pizza in the _____.
- Ⓐ sink
- Ⓑ oven
- Ⓒ curtains
- Ⓓ refrigerator

3. You often listen to the _____.
- Ⓐ lamp
- Ⓑ radio
- Ⓒ rug
- Ⓓ dresser

4. There are three _____ on the bed.
- Ⓐ pillows
- Ⓑ rugs
- Ⓒ lamps
- Ⓓ closets

5. There is a dog on the _____ in the living room.
- Ⓐ sofa
- Ⓑ lamp
- Ⓒ rug
- Ⓓ chair

➤ **Listen to the word. Find the word in the sentence. Mark each word.**

Example: *You hear:* bedrooms.
Our apartment has two bedrooms.
Ⓐ   Ⓑ   Ⓒ   ⬤

6. The house has two bathtubs.
Ⓐ   Ⓑ Ⓒ   Ⓓ

7. The armchair is in the living room.
Ⓐ   Ⓑ   Ⓒ   Ⓓ

8. Your backpack is on the bookcase.
Ⓐ   Ⓑ   Ⓒ   Ⓓ

9. There are ten classrooms in the school.
Ⓐ   Ⓑ   Ⓒ   Ⓓ

10. There is a bookcase in the kitchen.
Ⓐ   Ⓑ   Ⓒ   Ⓓ

Quiz: Chapter 4 *(continued)*

B. Vocabulary (20 points: 2 points each)

➤ **Find the word that names the picture.**

Example:

- Ⓐ bathroom
- Ⓑ house
- ⬤ living room
- Ⓓ apartment

11.

- Ⓐ cook
- Ⓑ eat
- Ⓒ lamp
- Ⓓ cabinet

12.

- Ⓐ sink
- Ⓑ sofa
- Ⓒ closet
- Ⓓ mirror

13.

- Ⓐ oven
- Ⓑ pillow
- Ⓒ radio
- Ⓓ window

14.

- Ⓐ lamp
- Ⓑ oven
- Ⓒ desk
- Ⓓ house

15.

- Ⓐ rug
- Ⓑ bookcase
- Ⓒ oven
- Ⓓ sofa

➤ **Find the word that best completes the sentence.**

Example: There are _____ in the windows.
- Ⓐ rugs
- Ⓑ sofas
- Ⓒ pillows
- ⬤ curtains

16. I _____ my teeth every morning.
- Ⓐ shower
- Ⓑ brush
- Ⓒ cook
- Ⓓ watch

17. You _____ in the bedroom.
- Ⓐ wash
- Ⓑ brush
- Ⓒ sleep
- Ⓓ fill

18. In the living room, I _____ TV.
- Ⓐ watch
- Ⓑ read
- Ⓒ do
- Ⓓ make

19. Tito eats his food at the _____ table.
- Ⓐ living room
- Ⓑ bathroom
- Ⓒ house
- Ⓓ kitchen

20. Do you _____ in the living room?
- Ⓐ brush your teeth
- Ⓑ cook
- Ⓒ study
- Ⓓ take a shower

VISIONS BASIC Assessment Program • Copyright © Heinle

Quiz: Chapter 4 *(continued)*

C. Grammar (20 points: 2 points each)

➤ **Find the word that best completes the sentence.**

Example: There _____ four chairs in the kitchen.

Ⓐ is

🅑 are

21. There _____ a big sofa in the living room.

Ⓐ is

Ⓑ are

22. There _____ dogs on my street.

Ⓐ is

Ⓑ are

23. There _____ three boys in our family.

Ⓐ is

Ⓑ are

24. There is one big _____ in my living room.

Ⓐ window

Ⓑ windows

25. There _____ two cars across the street.

Ⓐ is

Ⓑ are

26. There are five _____ in my apartment building.

Ⓐ cat

Ⓑ cats

27. There _____ a girl named Mia in my class.

Ⓐ is

Ⓑ are

28. There _____ cakes on the kitchen table.

Ⓐ is

Ⓑ are

29. There _____ a small mirror in the bathroom.

Ⓐ is

Ⓑ are

30. There are thirty _____ in November.

Ⓐ day

Ⓑ days

Name _____ Date _____

Quiz: Chapter 4 *(continued)*

D. Reading (20 points: 5 points each)

> **My Apartment**
>
> My apartment is large. It has a kitchen, a living room, a bathroom, and three bedrooms. There are two sofas and a chair in the living room. There is a bed with two pillows, a closet, and a bookcase in my bedroom. My apartment is the perfect home. It is my home.

➤ **Choose the best answer.**

Example: What is the paragraph about?
Ⓐ a house
Ⓑ a room
Ⓒ an apartment
Ⓓ a building

31. How big is the apartment?
Ⓐ not large
Ⓑ large
Ⓒ very small
Ⓓ small

32. How many bedrooms does the apartment have?
Ⓐ three
Ⓑ one
Ⓒ two
Ⓓ four

33. Where are the sofas in the apartment?
Ⓐ in the living room
Ⓑ in the kitchen
Ⓒ in the bedroom
Ⓓ on the stairs

34. What is the apartment like?
Ⓐ It is nice.
Ⓑ It is dark.
Ⓒ It is pink.
Ⓓ It is perfect.

E. Writing (20 points: #35–44, 1 point each; #45, 10 points)

➤ **Write the words that best complete the sentences.**

A: Where is your (**35.**) _____?
B: It's on Main Street.
A: Where do you watch TV?

B: I watch TV in (**36.**) _____.
A: What's in your bedroom?

B: There (**37.**) _____ one (**38.**)

_____ in my bedroom.

There (**39.**) _____ two (**40.**)

_____ in my bedroom.
A: What do you do in your bedroom?

B: I listen to (**41.**) _____ in my bedroom. Sometimes I (**42.**)

_____ in my bedroom. I

often (**43.**) _____ books in my bedroom. At night, I (**44.**)

_____ in my bedroom.

45. What is your favorite room in your home?

➤ **On a separate piece of paper, describe your favorite room. Write a short paragraph.**

VISIONS BASIC Assessment Program • Copyright © Heinle

Name _____ Date _____

Quiz: Chapter 5

A. Listening (20 points: 2 points each)

➤ **Listen to the sentence. Write the missing word.**

Example: *You hear:* The train comes at three o'clock.

The _____ comes at three o'clock.
- Ⓐ bus
- Ⓑ theater
- Ⓒ car
- 🅓 train

1. Oscar walks to the police _____.
- Ⓐ car
- Ⓑ station
- Ⓒ man
- Ⓓ center

2. How do you get to the _____?
- Ⓐ video store
- Ⓑ supermarket
- Ⓒ station
- Ⓓ mall

3. It is one _____.
- Ⓐ a quarter
- Ⓑ thirty
- Ⓒ twenty
- Ⓓ twelve

4. The _____ is on Third Street.
- Ⓐ restaurant
- Ⓑ store
- Ⓒ post office
- Ⓓ newspaper

5. The _____ is near the park.
- Ⓐ library
- Ⓑ supermarket
- Ⓒ movie theater
- Ⓓ fire station

➤ **Listen to the word. Choose the missing letters.**

Example: *You hear:* sh op.
- Ⓐ ch
- Ⓑ wh
- 🅒 sh
- Ⓓ th

6. ☐ in
- Ⓐ sh
- Ⓑ ch
- Ⓒ ng
- Ⓓ th

7. ☐ ank
- Ⓐ ch
- Ⓑ wh
- Ⓒ sh
- Ⓓ th

8. ri ☐
- Ⓐ th
- Ⓑ sh
- Ⓒ ng
- Ⓓ wh

9. fi ☐
- Ⓐ sh
- Ⓑ th
- Ⓒ ch
- Ⓓ ng

10. ☐ ere
- Ⓐ ch
- Ⓑ wh
- Ⓒ th
- Ⓓ sh

Name _____ Date _____

Quiz: Chapter 5 *(continued)*

B. Vocabulary (20 points: 2 points each)

➤ **Find the word that names the picture.**

Example:

Ⓐ restaurant
Ⓑ fire station
● hospital
Ⓓ house

11.
Ⓐ park
Ⓑ movie theater
Ⓒ post office
Ⓓ street

12.
Ⓐ moon
Ⓑ noon
Ⓒ quarter to
Ⓓ half past

13.
Ⓐ one fifteen
Ⓑ three thirty
Ⓒ one thirty
Ⓓ one twenty

14.
Ⓐ fire station
Ⓑ train
Ⓒ restaurant
Ⓓ library

15.
Ⓐ park
Ⓑ theater
Ⓒ supermarket
Ⓓ hospital

➤ **Find the word that best completes the sentence.**

Example: We _____ to the video store.
Ⓐ talk
Ⓑ shop
Ⓒ bus
● walk

16. Velma takes a _____ to work in the morning.
Ⓐ park
Ⓑ bus
Ⓒ walk
Ⓓ post office

17. Jeff works at the _____ on Second Street.
Ⓐ hospital
Ⓑ car
Ⓒ walk
Ⓓ train

18. Grandfather and Nia walk in the _____ every morning.
Ⓐ movie theater
Ⓑ supermarket
Ⓒ video store
Ⓓ park

19. In the _____ you can rent a movie.
Ⓐ post office
Ⓑ video store
Ⓒ hospital
Ⓓ restaurant

20. Do you shop at the _____?
Ⓐ fire station
Ⓑ community center
Ⓒ restaurant
Ⓓ mall

VISIONS BASIC Assessment Program • Copyright © Heinle

Quiz: Chapter 5 *(continued)*

C. Grammar (20 points: 2 points each)

➤ **Find the word that best completes the sentence.**

Example: She _____ shopping at the mall.

ⓐ am
🅑 is
ⓒ are
ⓓ be

21. I _____ reading a good book.
ⓐ is
ⓑ be
ⓒ are
ⓓ am

22. We _____ watching a video.
ⓐ are
ⓑ am
ⓒ be
ⓓ is

23. Oswaldo _____ dancing with Julia.
ⓐ be
ⓑ are
ⓒ am
ⓓ is

24. I _____ taking the train.
ⓐ are
ⓑ am
ⓒ is
ⓓ be

25. You _____ using the computer today.
ⓐ be
ⓑ is
ⓒ are
ⓓ am

26. They are _____ in the park.
ⓐ run
ⓑ running
ⓒ runing
ⓓ runs

27. Our team is _____ a game today.
ⓐ plays
ⓑ play
ⓒ player
ⓓ playing

28. Miranda is _____ to work today.
ⓐ drive
ⓑ driveing
ⓒ driving
ⓓ drives

29. Sam and Dan are _____ a video.
ⓐ rents
ⓑ renting
ⓒ rentting
ⓓ rent

30. _____ leaving on the bus.
ⓐ I are
ⓑ I're
ⓒ I'm
ⓓ I's

Quiz: Chapter 5 *(continued)*

D. Reading (20 points: 5 points each)

Poetry Reading

Authors Read at Library

Two authors are reading their books this week at Westfield Library. Writer Ann Diaz is reading poems from her book *My Town* at 2:15 on Wednesday. On Thursday at 1:30, Serge Miskin is showing pictures from his book *Community Colors*. Miskin is also reading stories and teaching a drawing class.

➤ **Choose the best answer.**

Example: What is the story about?
- Ⓐ Authors are leaving the library.
- Ⓑ Authors are writing in the library.
- Ⓒ Authors are reading in the library.
- Ⓓ Three authors are in the library.

31. Who are the authors?
- Ⓐ Ann Miskin and Serge Diaz
- Ⓑ Ann Diaz and *My Town*
- Ⓒ Serge Miskin and *Community Colors*
- Ⓓ Ann Diaz and Serge Mishkin

32. Which author is reading *My Town*?
- Ⓐ Ann Diaz
- Ⓑ Ann Miskin
- Ⓒ Ann Diaz and Serge Miskin
- Ⓓ Serge Miskin

33. Which author is teaching a class?
- Ⓐ Ann Diaz
- Ⓑ Serge Diaz
- Ⓒ Ann Diaz and Serge Miskin
- Ⓓ Serge Miskin

34. When is Ann Diaz reading?
- Ⓐ at 2:15 on Wednesday
- Ⓑ at one thirty on Wednesday
- Ⓒ at 2:15 on Thursday
- Ⓓ at two thirty on Wednesday

E. Writing (20 points: #35–44, 1 point each; #45, 10 points)

➤ **Write the words that best complete the sentences.**

Carol: How do you get to **(35.)** _____ every day?

Bob: I **(36.)** _____. How about you?

Carol: I usually **(37.)** _____. Sometimes I **(38.)** _____.

Bob: I usually leave at **(39.)** _____. How about you?

Carol: I leave at **(40.)** _____.

Bob: I get home at **(41.)** _____. How about you?

Carol: I get home at **(42.)** _____. Then I read **(43.)** _____. How about you?

Bob: I usually **(44.)** _____.

45. What are your friends and family members doing?

➤ **On a separate piece of paper, write a short paragraph. Say what five of your friends and family members are doing.**

VISIONS BASIC Assessment Program • Copyright © Heinle

Mid-Book Exam: Chapters 1–5

A. Listening (10 points: 1 point each)

➤ **Listen to the word. Find the word in the sentence. Mark each word.**

Example: *You hear:* address.

Write your address on the form.
Ⓐ   Ⓑ   ●   Ⓓ

1. Inez has beautiful blond, curly hair.
Ⓐ   Ⓑ   Ⓒ   Ⓓ

2. Do you exercise three times a week?
      Ⓐ   Ⓑ   Ⓒ   Ⓓ

3. There are sandwiches in the refrigerator.
  Ⓐ   Ⓑ   Ⓒ   Ⓓ

4. The post office is next to the hospital.
   Ⓐ   Ⓑ   Ⓒ   Ⓓ

5. My friend Jeff is tall and handsome.
     Ⓐ   Ⓑ   Ⓒ   Ⓓ

➤ **Listen to the word. Choose the word the rhymes with the word.**

Example: *You hear:* bug.
Ⓐ cup
Ⓑ bus
● rug
Ⓓ bag

6. Ⓐ sit
    Ⓑ right
    Ⓒ find
    Ⓓ weight

7. Ⓐ touch
    Ⓑ check
    Ⓒ teach
    Ⓓ cheek

8. Ⓐ skate
    Ⓑ man
    Ⓒ paint
    Ⓓ pan

9. Ⓐ sing
    Ⓑ thin
    Ⓒ long
    Ⓓ fine

10. Ⓐ mug
     Ⓑ map
     Ⓒ man
     Ⓓ cape

Name _____ Date _____

Mid-Book Exam *continued*

B. Vocabulary (20 points: 1 point each)

➤ **Read the words inside and outside the oval. Find the missing word.**

Example:

march ?
(months)
november may

- Ⓐ week
- Ⓑ Wednesday
- Ⓒ fall
- ⬤Ⓓ October

11.

mother sister
?
father brother

- Ⓐ school
- Ⓑ parent
- Ⓒ family
- Ⓓ friends

12.

? curly
(hair)
blonde straight

- Ⓐ heavy
- Ⓑ wavy
- Ⓒ happy
- Ⓓ tall

13.

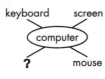

keyboard screen
(computer)
? mouse

- Ⓐ stapler
- Ⓑ telephone
- Ⓒ secretary
- Ⓓ printer

14.

soccer swim
(sports)
football ?

- Ⓐ feet
- Ⓑ shop
- Ⓒ baseball
- Ⓓ play the drums

15.

bathroom living room
(rooms)
? bedroom

- Ⓐ kitchen
- Ⓑ dresser
- Ⓒ curtain
- Ⓓ closet

➤ **Find the word that best completes the sentence.**

Example: Mica plays the _____.

- Ⓐ drums
- Ⓑ keyboard
- Ⓒ feet
- ⬤Ⓓ guitar

16. This is a _____.

- Ⓐ chair
- Ⓑ mirror
- Ⓒ curtain
- Ⓓ stapler

17 Sara likes to _____.

- Ⓐ job
- Ⓑ swim
- Ⓒ play drums
- Ⓓ paint

18. You can go to the _____ to get books.

- Ⓐ library
- Ⓑ cheese
- Ⓒ a job
- Ⓓ clothes

19. Marti takes the _____ to school.

- Ⓐ car
- Ⓑ walk
- Ⓒ train
- Ⓓ bus

20. This is a _____.

- Ⓐ train
- Ⓑ car
- Ⓒ bicycle
- Ⓓ street

VISIONS BASIC Assessment Program • Copyright © Heinle

Name _____ Date _____

Mid-Book Exam *continued*

➤ **Find the word that best completes the sentence.**

Example: My _____ were born in Brazil.
Ⓐ keyboard
🅑 parents
Ⓒ bird
Ⓓ secretary

21. Stephan's hair is not curly or wavy. It is _____.
Ⓐ long
Ⓑ black
Ⓒ medium length
Ⓓ straight

22. Tia likes music. She wants to play _____
Ⓐ soccer
Ⓑ an instrument
Ⓒ a sport
Ⓓ a video

23. On the computer, Andrei _____ to his friend.
Ⓐ writes a book
Ⓑ writes a video
Ⓒ writes e-mail
Ⓓ works

24. The sun _____ comes up in the morning.
Ⓐ always
Ⓑ never
Ⓒ usually
Ⓓ sometimes

25. After soccer practice, Giorgio takes a _____.
Ⓐ sofa
Ⓑ shower
Ⓒ bookcase
Ⓓ lamp

26. My grandfather goes to the _____ to see his doctor.
Ⓐ post office
Ⓑ supermarket
Ⓒ train
Ⓓ hospital

27. Nina _____ to school every day.
Ⓐ walk
Ⓑ park
Ⓒ walks
Ⓓ bus

28. Marc looks at the _____ to find the date.
Ⓐ copy machine
Ⓑ printer
Ⓒ telephone
Ⓓ calendar

29. Miguel's mother is tall and _____.
Ⓐ thin
Ⓑ think
Ⓒ wavy
Ⓓ height

30. The artist uses a _____ to make a picture.
Ⓐ baseball
Ⓑ drum
Ⓒ paintbrush
Ⓓ schedule

Name _____ Date _____

Mid-Book Exam *continued*

C. Grammar (20 points: 2 points each)

➤ **Find the word that best completes the sentence.**

Example: Edna is _____ grandmother.
- Ⓐ my
- Ⓑ you
- Ⓒ she
- Ⓓ hers

31. _____ and Millie play the guitar.
- Ⓐ You
- Ⓑ Your
- Ⓒ My
- Ⓓ Our

32. That is _____ new bicycle.
- Ⓐ he
- Ⓑ him
- Ⓒ hers
- Ⓓ his

33. Sonia and Isabel _____ in our family.
- Ⓐ is
- Ⓑ are
- Ⓒ am
- Ⓓ be

34. I _____ not a baseball player.
- Ⓐ am
- Ⓑ is
- Ⓒ are
- Ⓓ be

35. Patrick _____ soccer every Saturday.
- Ⓐ play
- Ⓑ plays
- Ⓒ playing
- Ⓓ player

36. Joanne and Sal _____ at the fire station.
- Ⓐ work
- Ⓑ works
- Ⓒ working
- Ⓓ is working

37. There _____ nine players on our baseball team.
- Ⓐ is
- Ⓑ are
- Ⓒ our
- Ⓓ am

38. There _____ a big window in the living room.
- Ⓐ is
- Ⓑ am
- Ⓒ are
- Ⓓ our

39. Davis and Ali _____ in the show.
- Ⓐ is dancing
- Ⓑ are dance
- Ⓒ are dancing
- Ⓓ is dance

40. Ronaldo _____ his favorite song in the show.
- Ⓐ is singing
- Ⓑ are singing
- Ⓒ sing
- Ⓓ singing

VISIONS BASIC Assessment Program • Copyright © Heinle

Mid-Book Exam *continued*

D. Reading (30 points: 2 points each)

Reading 1

Soccer Day

After school, Sonia sees the <u>sign</u> on the door. Then she sees her friend Isabel. "There is a soccer game today. Do you want to go?" Sonia says to Isabel.

"Yes!" says Isabel.

They go to the park. There is no soccer game.

"Where is the team?" Sonia says. "Oh no! Today is not Wednesday. Today is Tuesday!

"We will come back tomorrow!" Isabel says.

Soccer Game!

Watch our team.

Wilson Park

GAME: Wednesday, April 9, 4 p.m.

Call (501) 555-2535 for information.

➤ **Choose the best answer.**

41. In this story, the word <u>sign</u> means ___.
Ⓐ a face
Ⓑ a poster
Ⓒ a friend
Ⓓ a team

42. Sonia wants to ___.
Ⓐ play a musical instrument
Ⓑ be friends with Isabel
Ⓒ watch a soccer game
Ⓓ go to the park

43. When is the soccer game?
Ⓐ on Tuesday at 4 p.m.
Ⓑ on Tuesday, April 8
Ⓒ on Wednesday at 9 p.m.
Ⓓ on Wednesday at 4 p.m.

44. Sonia and Isabel go to the park but ___.
Ⓐ the team is not there
Ⓑ the team is there
Ⓒ the park is not open
Ⓓ the team is home

45. Sonia and Isabel come ___.
Ⓐ on the day after the game
Ⓑ on the day before the game
Ⓒ on the right day
Ⓓ at the right time

Name _____ Date _____

Mid-Book Exam *continued*

World's Tallest Buildings

Where do you live? Do you live in a house or in an apartment? On what floor do you live? Do you live on the first or second floor? Or are you higher up? Some people live and work very high up. How high? Right now the Petronas Twin Towers in Malaysia are the world's tallest buildings. These twin towers have 88 floors. From top to bottom they are 1,483 feet tall. That's as high as a mountain!

The Sears Tower in Chicago is the world's second tallest building. It has 110 floors and a height of 1,450 feet. Some people think that the Sears Tower is taller than the Petronas Towers. Its top floor is higher up than the top floor of Petronas Towers. But the <u>antennas</u> on top of the Petronas Towers are <u>taller</u> than the antenna of the Sears Tower.

Will there be taller buildings in the future? Workers right now are building a tower in Shanghai, China. It will be over 1,500 feet tall. And in Katangi, India, workers are making an even taller tower. It will have 224 <u>stories</u> and be over 2,000 feet tall. Now that's a big building!

VISIONS BASIC Assessment Program • Copyright © Heinle

World's Tallest Buildings

Building	Year Built	Floors	Height (ft)
Petronas Twin Towers, Malaysia	1998	88	1,483
Sears Tower, Chicago	1974	110	1,450
Jin Mao Building, Shanghai	1999	88	1,381
Empire State Building, New York	1931	102	1,250
Central Plaza, Hong Kong	1992	78	1,227
Bank of China Tower, Hong Kong	1989	70	1,209
T & C Tower, Kaoshiung, Taiwan	1997	85	1,140
Amoco Building, Chicago	1973	80	1,136
Central Station, Hong Kong	1998	79	1,135

Mid-Book Exam *continued*

➤ **Choose the best answer to each question.**

46. <u>Antennas</u> are ____.
   Ⓐ tall metal things on tops of buildings
   Ⓑ glass things on sides of buildings
   Ⓒ heavy things under buildings
   Ⓓ animals

47. In height, the tallest building ____.
   Ⓐ is the Sears tower
   Ⓑ are the Petronas Twin Towers
   Ⓒ is the Empire State Building
   Ⓓ is the Amoco Building

48. Which building has the most floors?
   Ⓐ the Sears Tower
   Ⓑ the Petronas Towers
   Ⓒ Central Plaza
   Ⓓ the Amoco Building

49. Which sentence is a fact?
   Ⓐ The Sears Tower is the best building.
   Ⓑ The Petronas Twin Towers are ugly.
   Ⓒ The Petronas Twin Towers are great.
   Ⓓ The Sears Tower is in Chicago.

50. The Empire State Building was built ____.
   Ⓐ after the Petronas Towers
   Ⓑ after the Sears Tower
   Ⓒ before the Petronas Towers
   Ⓓ after the T & C Tower

51. Most of the tall buildings are in ____.
   Ⓐ New York   Ⓒ Malaysia
   Ⓑ Hong Kong Ⓓ Chicago

52. The table is organized by ____.
   Ⓐ number of floors
   Ⓑ name of building
   Ⓒ height in feet
   Ⓓ year building was built

53. The word <u>stories</u> means ____.
   Ⓐ tales   Ⓒ floors
   Ⓑ walls   Ⓓ buildings

54. The Bank of China Tower has ____ floors.
   Ⓐ 88   Ⓒ 1,209
   Ⓑ 1989   Ⓓ 70

55. The Chrysler Building is not on the list. It is probably ____.
   Ⓐ less than 1,127 feet tall
   Ⓑ more than 90 floors
   Ⓒ in Chicago
   Ⓓ too tall

E. Writing (20 points: #56–65, 1 point each; #66, 10 points)

➤ **Write the words that best complete the sentences.**

I live in (**56.**) _____. I live (**57.**) _____ with my (**58.**) _____ I go to school at (**59.**) _____. At school I study (**60.**) _____ and (**61.**) _____ My favorite subject in school is (**62.**) _____.

My friend's name is (**63.**) _____ After school I like to (**64.**) _____ My favorite sport is (**65.**) _____.

66. What activities do you do?

➤ **On a separate piece of paper, write a paragraph. Talk about your activities. What do you do? When do you do them? Where do you do them? Who do you do them with?**

Name _____ Date _____

Mid-Book Exam *continued*

Speaking Assessment (100 points: 25 points each)
See Rubric for Speaking Assessment, p. xvi

This Speaking Assessment provides an opportunity to assess students speaking skills. To administer the test, have the student open to the indicated page in the student book. Ask the questions. The student is graded based on the Rubric for Speaking Assessment on p. xvi of this Assessment Guide.

67. Look at the Student Information Form on page 58. What is the girl's last name? What is her first name? What is her phone number? What is your last name? What is your first name? What is your zip code? What is your date of birth?

68. Look at the picture on page 66. Who is in the picture? What adjectives describe the mother? What adjectives describe the father? What adjectives describe the grandfather? What adjectives describe the sister? What adjectives describe you?

69. Look at the picture on page 94. What objects are in the kitchen? What objects are in the living room? What objects are in the bathroom? What objects are in the bedroom? What objects are in your bedroom?

70. Look at the picture on page 108. Point to the supermarket. How do you get to the supermarket? Point to the library. How do you get to the library? How do you get to school? What time to you get to school? What time do you go home?

✂ —

Spelling Assessment (100 points: 5 points each)

Each Spelling Assessment provides students with a list of words that test spelling skills. Students are expected to know how to spell both phonetically and by sight and memory. Students should show proficiency in applying spelling rules in appropriate situations. Mastery of vowels, consonants, syllables, silent letters, blends, word endings, patterns, and other fundamental spelling concepts should be demonstrated. To administer the test, read each word on the list and have the student spell it in writing.

1. white		**11.** bath
2. cute		**12.** she
3. read		**13.** June
4. shop		**14.** thin
5. sing		**15.** fish
6. phone		**16.** jog
7. tenth		**17.** stove
8. bookshelf		**18.** home
9. need		**19.** when
10. bed		**20.** take

VISIONS BASIC Assessment Program • Copyright © Heinle

Name _____ Date _____

QUIZ: Chapter 6

A. Listening (20 points: 2 points each)

➤ **Listen to the sentence. Choose the missing word.**

Example: *You hear:* I eat breakfast every morning.
I eat _____ every morning.
Ⓐ lunch
🅑 breakfast
Ⓒ food
Ⓓ cereal

1. For lunch, we have _____.
Ⓐ fish
Ⓑ steak
Ⓒ potatoes
Ⓓ spaghetti

2. Do you need a _____?
Ⓐ napkin
Ⓑ tablecloth
Ⓒ fork
Ⓓ lunch

3. I need a _____ and a knife.
Ⓐ spoon
Ⓑ plate
Ⓒ fork
Ⓓ soup

4. Every day, Phan eats _____ for breakfast.
Ⓐ eggs
Ⓑ cereal
Ⓒ soup
Ⓓ sandwich

5. I put some soup in a _____.
Ⓐ bowl
Ⓑ plate
Ⓒ table
Ⓓ bacon

➤ **Listen to the word. Find the word in the sentence. Mark each word.**

Example: *You hear:* chicken.
Mario is making a chicken sandwich.
Ⓐ   Ⓑ   ⬤   Ⓓ

6. Do you want tomatoes in the salad?
Ⓐ   Ⓑ   Ⓒ   Ⓓ

7. There is a bowl of beans and rice.
Ⓐ   Ⓑ   Ⓒ   Ⓓ

8. The restaurant has pizza and pasta.
Ⓐ   Ⓑ   Ⓒ   Ⓓ

9. Eggs and toast are good for breakfast.
Ⓐ   Ⓑ   Ⓒ   Ⓓ

10. Four sandwiches are on the table.
Ⓐ   Ⓑ   Ⓒ   Ⓓ

Name _____ Date _____

Quiz: Chapter 6 *continued*

B. Vocabulary (20 points: 2 points each)

➤ **Find the word that names the picture.**

Example:

- Ⓐ toast
- Ⓑ rice
- Ⓒ sandwich
- ● pizza

11.

- Ⓐ fish
- Ⓑ spaghetti
- Ⓒ sandwich
- Ⓓ cereal

12.

- Ⓐ bacon
- Ⓑ eggs
- Ⓒ chicken
- Ⓓ soup

13.

- Ⓐ spoon
- Ⓑ fork
- Ⓒ pencil
- Ⓓ napkin

14.

- Ⓐ steak
- Ⓑ sandwiches
- Ⓒ hamburger
- Ⓓ eggs

15.

- Ⓐ steak
- Ⓑ fish
- Ⓒ potatoes
- Ⓓ beans

➤ **Find the word that best completes the sentence.**

Example: I eat _____ at noon.
- ● lunch
- Ⓑ breakfast
- Ⓒ fork
- Ⓓ tablecloth

16. Irina cuts the meat with her _____.
- Ⓐ spoon
- Ⓑ knife
- Ⓒ glass
- Ⓓ skin

17. We had a green _____ with our dinner.
- Ⓐ toast
- Ⓑ pizza
- Ⓒ salad
- Ⓓ eggs

18. You eat soup with a _____.
- Ⓐ spoon
- Ⓑ knife
- Ⓒ fork
- Ⓓ bowl

19. She put green _____ in the rice.
- Ⓐ spoons
- Ⓑ glasses
- Ⓒ peas
- Ⓓ bacon

20. My favorite dinner is _____ and potatoes.
- Ⓐ chicken
- Ⓑ napkins
- Ⓒ breakfast
- Ⓓ midnight

VISIONS BASIC Assessment Program • Copyright © Heinle

Quiz: Chapter 6 *continued*

C. Grammar (20 points: 2 points each)

➤ **Find the word that best completes the sentence.**

Example: There are _____ in the bag.
Ⓐ an orange
Ⓑ one orange
⬤ three oranges
Ⓓ two orange

21. Dave and Lin eat _____ for breakfast.
Ⓐ cereals
Ⓑ two cereal
Ⓒ two cereals
Ⓓ cereal

22. Marla eats _____ every day.
Ⓐ some bananas
Ⓑ banana
Ⓒ some banana
Ⓓ many banana

23. There is _____ on the plate.
Ⓐ one hamburger
Ⓑ two hamburger
Ⓒ hamburgers
Ⓓ three hamburgers

24. My brother cooks _____ for our family.
Ⓐ rice
Ⓑ rices
Ⓒ some rices
Ⓓ many rice

25. Jerry is making two _____ for lunch.
Ⓐ sandwich
Ⓑ sandwiches
Ⓒ rice
Ⓓ soup

26. You eat _____ for breakfast.
Ⓐ egg
Ⓑ two egg
Ⓒ a lot of egg
Ⓓ two eggs

27. Take _____ from the bowl.
Ⓐ some fruit
Ⓑ some fruits
Ⓒ many fruits
Ⓓ much fruits

28. For dinner, I have _____ and bread.
Ⓐ some soups
Ⓑ a lot of soups
Ⓒ soups
Ⓓ soup

29. Linda has _____ of salad.
Ⓐ two bowl
Ⓑ bowl
Ⓒ two bowls
Ⓓ some bowl

30. I put _____ next to each plate.
Ⓐ fork
Ⓑ two forks
Ⓒ two fork
Ⓓ some fork

Name _____ Date _____

Quiz: Chapter 6 *continued*

D. Reading (20 points: 5 points each)

The Food Pyramid, by Ahmed Karch

Bread, cereal, rice, and pasta are at the bottom of the food pyramid. I usually eat four servings a day. Vegetables and fruits are next. I should eat more of them. I eat three servings from the milk, yogurt, and cheese group. I don't eat a lot of milk, poultry, fish, beans, eggs, and nuts. At the top of the pyramid are fats, oils, and sweets. It's not good to eat a lot from this group.

➤ **Choose the best answer.**

Example: Who is the author?
Ⓐ the U.S. Department of Agriculture
Ⓑ the food pyramid
Ⓒ Ahmed Karch
Ⓓ a teacher

31. How many servings a day does Ahmed eat from the bread, cereal, rice, and pasta group?
Ⓐ none
Ⓑ five
Ⓒ four
Ⓓ three

32. What foods should Ahmed eat more of?
Ⓐ fats, oils, and sweets
Ⓑ vegetables and fruits
Ⓒ meat
Ⓓ milk

33. How many servings a day does he eat from the milk, yogurt, and cheese group?
Ⓐ none
Ⓑ five
Ⓒ four
Ⓓ three

34. What foods are at the top of the food pyramid?
Ⓐ fats, oils, and sweets
Ⓑ fruits and sweets
Ⓒ milk, yogurt, and cheese
Ⓓ fruits and vegetables

B. Writing (20 points: #35–44, 1 point each; #45, 10 points)

➤ **Write the words that best complete the sentences.**

What I Eat

For breakfast, I eat **(35.)** _____,

(36.) _____, and

(37.) _____.

For lunch, I eat **(38.)** _____,

(39.) _____, and

(40.) _____.

For dinner, I eat **(41.)** _____,

(42.) _____, and

(43.) _____.

My favorite food is **(44.)** _____.

45. What is your favorite meal—breakfast, lunch, or dinner?

➤ **On a separate piece of paper, write a short paragraph. Name your favorite meal. Write what you usually and what you sometimes eat. Write what you use to eat each food.**

VISIONS BASIC Assessment Program • Copyright © Heinle

Name _____   Date _____

QUIZ: Chapter 7

A. Listening (20 points: 2 points each)

➤ **Listen to the sentence. Choose the missing word.**

Example: *You hear:* I pay with a check. I pay with a _____.
- Ⓐ cash
- Ⓑ CD
- ● check
- Ⓓ credit card

1. The _____ is in the store.
   - Ⓐ customer
   - Ⓑ person
   - Ⓒ man
   - Ⓓ woman

2. We use an _____ to get money.
   - Ⓐ credit card
   - Ⓑ ATM card
   - Ⓒ card
   - Ⓓ cash

3. What is the name of the _____?
   - Ⓐ customer
   - Ⓑ store
   - Ⓒ salesperson
   - Ⓓ credit card

4. I buy _____ with a credit card.
   - Ⓐ shirts
   - Ⓑ clothes
   - Ⓒ CDs
   - Ⓓ food

5. Do you have a _____?
   - Ⓐ quarter
   - Ⓑ dime
   - Ⓒ shirt
   - Ⓓ dollar

➤ **Listen to the word. Choose the best answer.**

Example: *You hear:* repaint. What is the prefix of this word?
- Ⓐ paint
- Ⓑ repa
- ● re
- Ⓓ pa

6. What is the root word of this word?
   - Ⓐ re
   - Ⓑ rew
   - Ⓒ write
   - Ⓓ ite

7. What does the prefix of this word mean?
   - Ⓐ about
   - Ⓑ again
   - Ⓒ view
   - Ⓓ see

8. What does this word mean?
   - Ⓐ tell
   - Ⓑ tell again
   - Ⓒ do not tell
   - Ⓓ see again

9. In this word, the *re* comes _____.
   - Ⓐ after the root word *count*
   - Ⓑ before the root word *count*
   - Ⓒ before the prefix *count*
   - Ⓓ after the prefix *count*

10. What does this word mean?
    - Ⓐ pay for something
    - Ⓑ pay for something first
    - Ⓒ pay for something new
    - Ⓓ pay for something again

Name _____ Date _____

Quiz: Chapter 7 *continued*

B. Vocabulary (20 points: 2 points each)

➤ **Find the word that names the picture.**

Example:

ⓐ dime
ⓑ dollar
ⓒ penny
🅓 nickel

11.

ⓐ dollar
ⓑ ATM card
ⓒ cash
ⓓ coin

12.

ⓐ customer
ⓑ person
ⓒ price
ⓓ check

13.

ⓐ twenty dollar bill
ⓑ coin
ⓒ one dollar bill
ⓓ five dollar bill

14.

ⓐ check
ⓑ cash
ⓒ coin
ⓓ dollar

15.

ⓐ dollar
ⓑ dime
ⓒ gold
ⓓ bill

➤ **Find the word that best completes the sentence.**

Example: One _____ is twenty-five cents.
ⓐ dime
ⓑ nickel
🅒 quarter
ⓓ dollar

16. A _____ works in a store.
ⓐ sales
ⓑ salesperson
ⓒ customer
ⓓ buy

17. I am writing a _____ to pay for the clothes.
ⓐ check
ⓑ credit card
ⓒ cash
ⓓ ATM card

18. I use a _____ to pay for CDs.
ⓐ cash
ⓑ credit card
ⓒ price
ⓓ change

19. What is the _____ of these shoes?
ⓐ price
ⓑ dollar
ⓒ money
ⓓ cash

20. I have ten dollars in _____.
ⓐ coin
ⓑ credit card
ⓒ cash
ⓓ check

VISIONS BASIC Assessment Program • Copyright © Heinle

Quiz: Chapter 7 *continued*

C. Grammar (20 points: 2 points each)

➤ **Find the word that best completes the sentence.**

Example: Olga is ____ than Chad.
Ⓐ tall
🅑 taller
Ⓒ more taller
Ⓓ tallest

21. Shoes are _____ than socks.
Ⓐ expensive
Ⓑ expensiver
Ⓒ more expensiver
Ⓓ more expensive

22. Ricky is _____ than his father.
Ⓐ handsome
Ⓑ more handsome
Ⓒ handsomer
Ⓓ more handsomer

23. Milk is _____ than a hamburger.
Ⓐ cheaper
Ⓑ cheap
Ⓒ more cheaper
Ⓓ cheaping

24. I am _____ this year than last year.
Ⓐ happy
Ⓑ more happier
Ⓒ happier
Ⓓ happyer

25. A sofa is ____ than a rug.
Ⓐ important
Ⓑ importanter
Ⓒ more important
Ⓓ more importanter

26. A slice of pizza is _____ than a whole pizza.
Ⓐ more expensiver
Ⓑ cheaper
Ⓒ more cheaper
Ⓓ expensive

27. The red shirt is _____ than the green shirt.
Ⓐ bigger
Ⓑ more bigger
Ⓒ more smaller
Ⓓ small

28. My brother Dave is _____ than my sister Nell.
Ⓐ old
Ⓑ older
Ⓒ more younger
Ⓓ young

29. Our new apartment is _____ than our old house.
Ⓐ smaller
Ⓑ more bigger
Ⓒ big
Ⓓ more smaller

30. Water is _____ than milk.
Ⓐ thinner
Ⓑ thin
Ⓒ expensiver
Ⓓ more cheaper

Name _____   Date _____

Quiz: Chapter 7 *continued*

D. Reading (20 points: 5 points each)

King Vitas and the Cheaper Touch

King Vitas has the Cheaper Touch. Everything he touches gets cheaper. A $10 lunch turns into a $1 lunch! An expensive sweater turns into a cheap sweater! "I like this!" King Vitas says. But his money also gets cheaper. A ten-dollar bill turns into a one-dollar bill. In the end, everything is the same. King Vitas is not happier. He is not sadder.

➤ **Choose the best answer.**

Example: What is the story about?
Ⓐ King Midas
Ⓑ sweaters
Ⓒ the Cheaper Touch
Ⓓ King Vitas

31. What is the king's name?
Ⓐ the Golden Touch
Ⓑ King Vitas
Ⓒ the Cheaper Touch
Ⓓ no money

32. What special power does the king have?
Ⓐ Everything he touches gets cheaper.
Ⓑ Everything he touches turns to gold.
Ⓒ Everything he touches costs one dollar.
Ⓓ Everything he touches gets expensive.

33. What happens to the king's money?
Ⓐ It gets cheaper.
Ⓑ It gets bigger.
Ⓒ It turns to gold.
Ⓓ He can eat his money.

34. How does the story end?
Ⓐ King Vitas is sad.
Ⓑ King Vitas gets his wish.
Ⓒ Everything is the same for King Vitas.
Ⓓ Everything is different for King Vitas.

B. Writing (20 points: #35–44, 1 point each; #45, 10 points)

➤ **Write the words that best complete the sentences.**

I **(35.)** _____ for things in three ways. Sometimes, I pay with **(36.)** _____. Sometimes, I **(37.)** _____ a **(38.)** _____ or use a **(39.)** _____. I also use my **(40.)** _____ to get money from the bank.

When I buy things, I look first at the **(41.)** _____.

(42.) _____ things cost more than **(43.)** _____ things. Sometimes I use my money to buy **(44.)** _____.

45. You have one hundred dollars. What can you buy?

➤ **On a separate piece of paper, write a short paragraph. Say what you can buy and how much the things cost. Compare the prices. What is cheaper? What is more expensive?**

VISIONS BASIC Assessment Program • Copyright © Heinle

Name _____ Date _____

QUIZ: Chapter 8

A. Listening (20 points: 2 points each)

➤ **Listen to the word. Find the word in the sentence. Mark each word.**

Example: *You hear:* doctor.
Haluc wants to be a doctor or
     Ⓐ   Ⓑ   ●

an astronaut.
  Ⓓ

1. The chef is preparing a good meal for us.
    Ⓐ   Ⓑ   Ⓒ Ⓓ

2. Anita gives the cashier ten dollars.
    Ⓐ   Ⓑ Ⓒ Ⓓ

3. The artist draws a picture of a house.
    Ⓐ Ⓑ   Ⓒ   Ⓓ

4. Our waiter today is named Oscar.
  Ⓐ Ⓑ Ⓒ   Ⓓ

5. The clerk shows us where things are.
    Ⓐ Ⓑ   Ⓒ   Ⓓ

➤ **Listen to the word. Choose the best answer.**

Example: *You hear:* painter.
What is the suffix of this word?
Ⓐ paint
● er
Ⓒ ter
Ⓓ pain

6. What is the root word of this word?
Ⓐ garden
Ⓑ gard
Ⓒ er
Ⓓ den

7. What does the suffix of this word mean?
Ⓐ someone who writes
Ⓑ someone who manages
Ⓒ someone who sees something
Ⓓ someone who does something

8. What does this word mean?
Ⓐ someone who likes songs
Ⓑ someone who sings songs
Ⓒ someone who writes songs
Ⓓ someone who plays music

9. In this word, the *er* comes _____.
Ⓐ after the root word *dance*
Ⓑ before the root word *dance*
Ⓒ before the suffix *dance*
Ⓓ after the suffix *dance*

10. What does this word mean?
Ⓐ someone who takes care of children
Ⓑ someone who likes children
Ⓒ someone who cares about children
Ⓓ someone who works in a high school

Name _____ Date _____

Quiz: Chapter 8 *continued*

B. Vocabulary (20 points: 2 points each)

➤ **Find the word that names the picture.**

Example:

 Ⓐ cashier
 Ⓑ firefighter
 Ⓒ chef
 🔘 hairstylist

11.

 Ⓐ cashier
 Ⓑ painter
 Ⓒ astronaut
 Ⓓ doctor

12.

 Ⓐ carpenter
 Ⓑ musician
 Ⓒ clerk
 Ⓓ mechanic

13.

 Ⓐ carpenter
 Ⓑ firefighter
 Ⓒ chef
 Ⓓ artist

14.

 Ⓐ astronaut
 Ⓑ doctor
 Ⓒ firefighter
 Ⓓ artist

15.

 Ⓐ waiter
 Ⓑ astronaut
 Ⓒ mechanic
 Ⓓ clerk

➤ **Find the word that best completes the sentence.**

Example: The clerk weighs things on _____.
 Ⓐ hammer
 Ⓑ weight
 🔘 scales
 Ⓓ tray

16. This musician plays the _____.
 Ⓐ tray
 Ⓑ flute
 Ⓒ clay
 Ⓓ wrench

17. The waiter serves food on a _____.
 Ⓐ tray
 Ⓑ clay
 Ⓒ scales
 Ⓓ wrench

18. The carpenter uses a _____ and nails.
 Ⓐ scales
 Ⓑ suit
 Ⓒ hammer
 Ⓓ thermometer

19. An artist can make something out of _____.
 Ⓐ food
 Ⓑ nails
 Ⓒ thermometer
 Ⓓ clay

20. The mechanic fixes cars with a _____.
 Ⓐ French
 Ⓑ wrench
 Ⓒ hammer
 Ⓓ flute

VISIONS BASIC Assessment Program • Copyright © Heinle

Quiz: Chapter 8 *continued*

C. Grammar (20 points: 2 points each)

➤ **Find the word that best completes the sentence.**

Example: Maria is my friend. I like _____.
- Ⓐ she
- Ⓑ her
- Ⓒ him
- Ⓓ it

21. Tom and Joe are my friends. I meet _____ at school.
- Ⓐ him
- Ⓑ they
- Ⓒ them
- Ⓓ he

22. Mr. Santiago is a teacher. I have ____ for math.
- Ⓐ him
- Ⓑ he
- Ⓒ her
- Ⓓ it

23. He has a new car. He drives ____ to work every day.
- Ⓐ him
- Ⓑ her
- Ⓒ them
- Ⓓ it

24. My sister lives in Texas. I call _____ often on the telephone.
- Ⓐ her
- Ⓑ him
- Ⓒ them
- Ⓓ us

25. My mother is at the supermarket. She is buying _____ food for dinner.
- Ⓐ we
- Ⓑ ours
- Ⓒ you
- Ⓓ us

➤ **Which pronoun do you use for the underlined words?**

Example: I like <u>animals</u>.
- Ⓐ it
- Ⓑ them
- Ⓒ him
- Ⓓ they

26. Mr. Tejeda cooks dinner for <u>the family</u>.
- Ⓐ him
- Ⓑ her
- Ⓒ we
- Ⓓ them

27. I use <u>the computers</u> in the library.
- Ⓐ it
- Ⓑ they
- Ⓒ them
- Ⓓ us

28. My mother is taking <u>Debbie and me</u> to a show.
- Ⓐ them
- Ⓑ us
- Ⓒ we
- Ⓓ our

29. I play with <u>a soccer player named Marisa</u>.
- Ⓐ her
- Ⓑ him
- Ⓒ them
- Ⓓ she

30. The doctor is taking care of <u>my sister</u>.
- Ⓐ him
- Ⓑ her
- Ⓒ us
- Ⓓ we

Name _____ Date _____

Quiz: Chapter 8 *continued*

D. Reading (20 points: 5 points each)

┌───┐
│   **How to Order Fast-Food**   │
│   │
│   First, look at the menu, and don't be funny. │
│ Then make sure—do you have any money?   │
│ Then give your order: a hamburger with cheese. │
│ Speak slowly and clearly   │
│ and remember to say *please!*   │
└───┘

➤ **Choose the best answer.**

Example: What is the poem about?
Ⓐ how to take a fast-food order
Ⓑ how to give a fast-food order
Ⓒ how to eat fast-food
Ⓓ how to make fast-food

31. What is the first step?
Ⓐ Look at the menu.
Ⓑ Make sure you have money.
Ⓒ Say *please.*
Ⓓ Speak slowly and clearly.

32. What is the second step?
Ⓐ Say *please.*
Ⓑ Make sure you have money.
Ⓒ Look at the menu.
Ⓓ Speak slowly and clearly.

33. What is the third step?
Ⓐ Say *please.*
Ⓑ Speak slowly and clearly.
Ⓒ Look at the menu.
Ⓓ Give your order.

34. What is the last step?
Ⓐ Say *please.*
Ⓑ Speak slowly and clearly.
Ⓒ Look at the menu.
Ⓓ Give your order.

E. Writing (20 points: #35–44, 1 point each; #45, 10 points)

➤ **Write the words that best complete the sentences.**

Jobs

Many of the people I know have jobs.

My **(35.)** _____ is

(36.) _____. My

(37.) _____ is **(38.)** _____.

One of my friends is **(39.)** _____.

A **(40.)** _____ works at a

hospital. A **(41.)** _____ builds

houses. A **(42.)** _____ works at

a fire station. A **(43.)** _____

cooks food at a restaurant. A

(44.) _____ works at a

supermarket.

45. What job do you know about?

➤ **On a separate piece of paper, write a short paragraph. Talk about the job, what the person does, and what tools or objects the person uses.**

VISIONS BASIC Assessment Program • Copyright © Heinle

Name _____ Date _____

QUIZ: Chapter 9

A. Listening (20 points: 2 points each)

➤ **Listen to the sentence. Choose the missing word.**

Example: *You hear:* We see the fireworks in the sky.
We see the _____ in the sky.
- Ⓐ barbecue
- Ⓑ flowers
- Ⓒ stuffing
- Ⓓ fireworks

1. After dinner, Sid opened a box of _____.
- Ⓐ parade
- Ⓑ chocolates
- Ⓒ radio
- Ⓓ pie

2. There is _____ inside the turkey.
- Ⓐ stuffing
- Ⓑ pie
- Ⓒ chocolate
- Ⓓ parade

3. The _____ on the Fourth of July is beautiful.
- Ⓐ heart
- Ⓑ parade
- Ⓒ special
- Ⓓ flowers

4. On Valentine's Day, Steve got a _____ from Jan.
- Ⓐ card
- Ⓑ heart
- Ⓒ parade
- Ⓓ turkey

5. Pink and yellow _____ grow in the garden.
- Ⓐ chocolates
- Ⓑ cards
- Ⓒ hearts
- Ⓓ flowers

➤ **Listen to the word. Which word has the same sound?**

Example: *You hear:* spill.
Which word has the same *s* blend sound?
- Ⓐ sport
- Ⓑ skin
- Ⓒ story
- Ⓓ six

6. Which word has the same *s* blend sound?
- Ⓐ special
- Ⓑ spark
- Ⓒ story
- Ⓓ skip

7. Which word has the same *s* blend sound?
- Ⓐ spin
- Ⓑ skate
- Ⓒ streaking
- Ⓓ splashing

8. Which word has the same *s* blend sound?
- Ⓐ spark
- Ⓑ stairs
- Ⓒ skirt
- Ⓓ story

9. Which word has the same *s* blend sound?
- Ⓐ ski
- Ⓑ stuffing
- Ⓒ special
- Ⓓ spend

10. Which word has the same *s* blend sound?
- Ⓐ spoon
- Ⓑ sat
- Ⓒ stuffing
- Ⓓ sail

Name _____ Date _____

Quiz: Chapter 9 *continued*

B. Vocabulary (20 points: 2 points each)

➤ **Find the word that names the picture.**

Example:

ⓐ American flag
ⓑ barbecue
ⓒ pie
ⓓ flowers

11.

ⓐ chocolates
ⓑ fireworks
ⓒ flowers
ⓓ pie

12.

ⓐ card
ⓑ flowers
ⓒ heart
ⓓ turkey

13.

ⓐ New Year's Day
ⓑ Mother's Day
ⓒ President's Day
ⓓ Halloween

14.

ⓐ parade
ⓑ card
ⓒ Thanksgiving
ⓓ New Year's Day

15.

ⓐ Earth Day
ⓑ fireworks
ⓒ turkey
ⓓ flowers

➤ **Find the word that best completes the sentence.**

Example: These pink _____ are beautiful.
ⓐ chocolates
🅑 flowers
ⓒ turkeys
ⓓ parades

16. The apple _____ is delicious!
ⓐ parade
ⓑ pie
ⓒ turkey
ⓓ flowers

17. Write your name on the _____.
ⓐ barbecue
ⓑ flowers
ⓒ New Year's Day
ⓓ card

18. We celebrate Lincoln's birthday on _____.
ⓐ President's Day
ⓑ Earth Day
ⓒ Father's Day
ⓓ Mother's Day

19. Are we having hamburgers at the _____?
ⓐ parade
ⓑ barbecue
ⓒ Earth Day
ⓓ flowers

20. Mrs. Brown gets cards from her children on _____.
ⓐ Father's Day
ⓑ parade
ⓒ stuffing
ⓓ Mother's Day

VISIONS BASIC Assessment Program • Copyright © Heinle

Quiz: Chapter 9 *continued*

C. Grammar (20 points: 2 points each)

➤ **Find the word that best completes the sentence.**

Example: Jay _____ in school last week.
- Ⓐ were
- ⬤Ⓑ was
- Ⓒ is
- Ⓓ are

21. Mimi _____ at the Post Office last year.
- Ⓐ work
- Ⓑ works
- Ⓒ worked
- Ⓓ working

22. Yesterday, I _____ tennis with Lance.
- Ⓐ plaied
- Ⓑ play
- Ⓒ plays
- Ⓓ played

23. The students _____ for the test all year.
- Ⓐ studied
- Ⓑ studying
- Ⓒ studyed
- Ⓓ studies

24. James _____ the living room walls.
- Ⓐ paint
- Ⓑ painted
- Ⓒ painting
- Ⓓ painter

25. Steve and Paul _____ on the team last year.
- Ⓐ was
- Ⓑ are
- Ⓒ were
- Ⓓ am

26. You _____ in your office yesterday.
- Ⓐ was
- Ⓑ were
- Ⓒ is
- Ⓓ are

27. I _____ Hector's cherry pie.
- Ⓐ loves
- Ⓑ loving
- Ⓒ loveed
- Ⓓ loved

28. Thanksgiving _____ at our house last year.
- Ⓐ was
- Ⓑ are
- Ⓒ were
- Ⓓ is

29. At the end, Kate _____ with Theo.
- Ⓐ dance
- Ⓑ dancing
- Ⓒ danced
- Ⓓ danceed

30. I _____ the book more than the video.
- Ⓐ liked
- Ⓑ likd
- Ⓒ likes
- Ⓓ liking

Name _____   Date _____

Quiz: Chapter 9 *continued*

D. Reading (20 points: 5 points each)

Washington Trip, by Tran Lee

On the Fourth of July, my class was in Washington, D.C. There were fireworks. There was also a parade. At night, there was a barbecue. I played at the Mall and listened to music. The Mall was where Martin Luther King Jr. organized his most famous protest in 1963. This trip was a lot of fun!

➤ **Choose the best answer.**

Example: What is the story about?
Ⓐ a trip to Atlanta, Georgia
Ⓑ Martin Luther King Jr.
◉ a trip to Washington, D.C.
Ⓓ a protest

31. When was the trip?
Ⓐ on Martin Luther King Jr. Day
Ⓑ on Thanksgiving
Ⓒ on a Saturday
Ⓓ on the Fourth of July

32. What is one thing that the writer did?
Ⓐ played music
Ⓑ listened to a speech
Ⓒ listened to music
Ⓓ marched in a parade

33. What happened in 1963?
Ⓐ Martin Luther King Jr. was born.
Ⓑ Washington organized a protest.
Ⓒ Martin Luther King Jr. organized a protest.
Ⓓ There was a parade.

34. Who is the writer of the story?
Ⓐ Martin Luther King Jr.
Ⓑ George Washington
Ⓒ Abraham Lincoln
Ⓓ Tran Lee

E. Writing (20 points: #35–44, 1 point each; #45, 10 points)

➤ **Write the words that best complete the sentences.**

Holidays

In January, **(35.)** _____ is the first holiday of the year. Next comes **(36.)** _____ and **(37.)** _____ in February. In May and June we have **(38.)** _____ and **(39.)** _____. Then on July 4 is **(40.)** _____. This holiday is fun because of **(41.)** _____. Next comes **(42.)** _____ in October and **(43.)** _____ in November. I like this holiday because **(44.)**

_____.

45. What is your favorite holiday?

➤ **On a separate piece of paper, write a short paragraph. Name your favorite holiday. How do you celebrate it? What do you see and do?**

Name _____ Date _____

QUIZ: Chapter 10

A. Listening (20 points: 2 points each)

➤ **Listen to the word. Find the word in the sentence. Mark each word.**

Example: Amir is excited about
            Ⓐ   Ⓑ

his new job.
  Ⓒ Ⓓ

1. Sidney yawns when he is bored.
   Ⓐ   Ⓑ   Ⓒ   Ⓓ

2. When I am embarrassed, I always blush.
    Ⓐ   Ⓑ   Ⓒ   Ⓓ

3. Clara smiles when she is happy.
   Ⓐ   Ⓑ   Ⓒ   Ⓓ

4. Ann is never sad or bored.
   Ⓐ   Ⓑ   Ⓒ   Ⓓ

5. If you need help, just shout.
      Ⓐ   Ⓑ   Ⓒ   Ⓓ

➤ **Listen to the word. Which word rhymes with the word?**

Example: *You hear:* rose.
- Ⓐ nose
- Ⓑ toss
- Ⓒ boat
- Ⓓ does

6. Ⓐ late
   Ⓑ beat
   Ⓒ hat
   Ⓓ date

7. Ⓐ far
   Ⓑ near
   Ⓒ bar
   Ⓓ her

8. Ⓐ dish
   Ⓑ push
   Ⓒ wash
   Ⓓ ship

9. Ⓐ rug
   Ⓑ right
   Ⓒ sun
   Ⓓ say

10. Ⓐ green
    Ⓑ then
    Ⓒ bean
    Ⓓ mean

Name _____   Date _____

Quiz: Chapter 10 *continued*

B. Vocabulary (20 points: 2 points each)

➤ **Find the word that names the picture.**

Example:

- Ⓐ excited
- Ⓑ blush
- ⬤ bored
- Ⓓ happy

11.
- Ⓐ sad
- Ⓑ mad
- Ⓒ cry
- Ⓓ smile

12.
- Ⓐ shout
- Ⓑ shake
- Ⓒ laugh
- Ⓓ yawn

13.
- Ⓐ shy
- Ⓑ laugh
- Ⓒ happy
- Ⓓ mad

14.
- Ⓐ shout
- Ⓑ scared
- Ⓒ sad
- Ⓓ yawn

15.
- Ⓐ cry
- Ⓑ jump
- Ⓒ yawn
- Ⓓ laugh

➤ **Find the word that best completes the sentence.**

Example: I _____ when I am embarrassed.
- Ⓐ shout
- Ⓑ sleep
- ⬤ blush
- Ⓓ walk

16. Evan was scared and he started to _____.
- Ⓐ laugh
- Ⓑ shake
- Ⓒ leave
- Ⓓ hope

17. When she is happy, Uma has a big _____.
- Ⓐ smile
- Ⓑ skirt
- Ⓒ sun
- Ⓓ jump

18. The baby____ when he is sad.
- Ⓐ shake
- Ⓑ hurt
- Ⓒ makes
- Ⓓ cries

19. Florina was _____ to see her sister at school.
- Ⓐ surprised
- Ⓑ bored
- Ⓒ mad
- Ⓓ good

20. Mom was ____ when I lost the money.
- Ⓐ made
- Ⓑ mad
- Ⓒ happy
- Ⓓ embarrassed

VISIONS BASIC Assessment Program • Copyright © Heinle

Name _____ Date _____

Quiz: Chapter 10 *continued*

C. Grammar (20 points: 2 points each)

➤ **Which word best completes the sentence?**

Example: Molly _____ in the concert next Friday.
Ⓐ will sings
Ⓑ sang
Ⓒ will sing
Ⓓ sing

21. Molly's grandmother _____ her sing for the first time.
Ⓐ hear
Ⓑ will hear
Ⓒ will heard
Ⓓ will hears

22. The Tigers _____ the Bears in the game tomorrow.
Ⓐ will play
Ⓑ played
Ⓒ plays
Ⓓ will played

23. We _____ when we see Jeremy.
Ⓐ will smiles
Ⓑ will smile
Ⓒ smiled
Ⓓ smiling

24. You _____ when you see this movie.
Ⓐ cried
Ⓑ will cries
Ⓒ crying
Ⓓ will cry

25. I _____ for you at the game.
Ⓐ will looked
Ⓑ will look
Ⓒ looks
Ⓓ will looks

➤ **Change the sentence to the future. Replace the underlined words.**

Example: Steve <u>liked</u> the movie very much.
Ⓐ will liked
Ⓑ will like
Ⓒ will likes
Ⓓ like

26. When school ends, everyone <u>smiles</u>.
Ⓐ will smiled
Ⓑ will smile
Ⓒ will smiling
Ⓓ will smiles

27. Tara <u>played</u> the guitar at the club.
Ⓐ will play
Ⓑ will played
Ⓒ will plays
Ⓓ play

28. You <u>know</u> her when you see her.
Ⓐ knowed
Ⓑ will knows
Ⓒ will knowing
Ⓓ will know

29. They <u>rented</u> three videos from the video store.
Ⓐ will rents
Ⓑ will rented
Ⓒ will rent
Ⓓ rents

30. <u>I am</u> in ninth grade.
Ⓐ I'm be
Ⓑ I'd
Ⓒ I'll be
Ⓓ I'm am

Name _____ Date _____

Quiz: Chapter 10 *continued*

D. Reading (20 points: 5 points each)

> **When Middle School Ends,** by Jed Juarez
>
> What will I be
> when middle school ends?
> Will I be tall? Will I have friends?
> Will I still laugh? Will I know how?
> Will I be the same person
> that I am right now?

➤ **Choose the best answer.**

Example: Who is the writer of the poem?
- Ⓐ Ted Jiminez
- Ⓑ Middle School
- Ⓒ Mel Glenn
- Ⓓ Jed Juarez

31. Who is the poem about?
- Ⓐ a high school student
- Ⓑ a father of a high school student
- Ⓒ a middle school student
- Ⓓ the mother of a middle school student

32. What is the writer writing about?
- Ⓐ the end of high school
- Ⓑ the end of middle school
- Ⓒ the beginning of middle school
- Ⓓ the beginning of high school

33. What question does the writer ask?
- Ⓐ Will I be happy?
- Ⓑ Will I have good grades?
- Ⓒ Will I play sports?
- Ⓓ Will I have friends?

34. What does the writer want to know?
- Ⓐ if he'll be on the soccer team
- Ⓑ if he'll still be the same person
- Ⓒ if he'll like high school
- Ⓓ if he'll learn to play the drums

E. Writing (20 points: #35–44, 1 point each; #45, 10 points)

➤ **Write the words that best complete the sentences.**

The Movie

I went to a new movie yesterday. I was **(35.)** _____. My favorite star, **(36.)** _____, was in the movie. We waited an hour for the movie to start. I was **(37.)** _____. I **(38.)** _____ a lot.

Finally, the movie started. The star played a **(39.)** _____ in the movie who was **(40.)** _____. There were a lot of funny parts in the movie. I **(41.)** _____ a lot. There were some **(42.)** _____ parts that made me **(43.)** _____. When the movie was finished, I felt **(44.)** _____.

45. What are your feelings?

➤ **On a separate piece of paper, write a short paragraph about your feelings. How do you feel in the morning, in the afternoon, and at night? How do you act?**

VISIONS BASIC Assessment Program • Copyright © Heinle

End-of-Book Exam: Chapters 6–10

A. Listening (10 points: 1 point each)

➤ **Listen to the word. Find the word in the sentence. Mark the word.**

Example: *You hear:* breakfast.

She eats breakfast at eight o'clock.
Ⓐ   ⬤Ⓑ   Ⓒ   Ⓓ

1. I have a nickel, a quarter, and a dime.
Ⓐ   Ⓑ   Ⓒ   Ⓓ

2. You can pay in cash or write a check.
     Ⓐ   Ⓑ   Ⓒ   Ⓓ

3. The chef makes excellent pasta dishes.
     Ⓐ   Ⓑ   Ⓒ   Ⓓ

4. The American flag has fifty stars.
     Ⓐ   Ⓑ   Ⓒ   Ⓓ

5. The movie made me feel very scared.
     Ⓐ   Ⓑ   Ⓒ   Ⓓ

➤ **Listen to the sentence. Choose the missing word.**

Example: I _____ my favorite book when I am bored.
Ⓐ reader
Ⓑ repay
Ⓒ repaint
⬤Ⓓ reread

6. Our family eats _____ every night.
Ⓐ rice
Ⓑ rices
Ⓒ race
Ⓓ right

7. When will the _____ finish your house?
Ⓐ straight
Ⓑ painter
Ⓒ pay
Ⓓ writer

8. I _____ we will win the next game.
Ⓐ think
Ⓑ thin
Ⓒ thinner
Ⓓ this

9. To make a salad, I need two _____.
Ⓐ tomatoes
Ⓑ potato
Ⓒ potatoes
Ⓓ tomato

10. You need to _____ this paragraph.
Ⓐ writer
Ⓑ repay
Ⓒ rewrite
Ⓓ rewriter

Name _____   Date _____

End-of-Book Exam *continued*

B. Vocabulary (20 points: 1 point each)

➤ **Read the words inside and outside the oval. Find the missing word.**

Example:

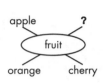

- Ⓐ rice
- Ⓑ potato
- Ⓒ vegetable
- Ⓓ banana

11.

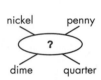

- Ⓐ dollars
- Ⓑ bills
- Ⓒ coins
- Ⓓ credit card

12.

- Ⓐ hospital
- Ⓑ change
- Ⓒ firefighter
- Ⓓ brother

13.

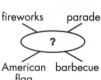

- Ⓐ Halloween
- Ⓑ Fourth of July
- Ⓒ Thanksgiving
- Ⓓ Valentine's Day

14.

- Ⓐ special
- Ⓑ smooth
- Ⓒ slow
- Ⓓ embarrased

15.

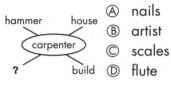

- Ⓐ nails
- Ⓑ artist
- Ⓒ scales
- Ⓓ flute

16.

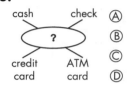

- Ⓐ penny
- Ⓑ repay
- Ⓒ money
- Ⓓ credit

17.

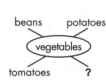

- Ⓐ peas
- Ⓑ rice
- Ⓒ bacon
- Ⓓ hamburger

18.

- Ⓐ cents
- Ⓑ coins
- Ⓒ bills
- Ⓓ checks

19.

- Ⓐ change
- Ⓑ flowers
- Ⓒ scissors
- Ⓓ five dollar bill

20.

- Ⓐ times
- Ⓑ facts
- Ⓒ opinions
- Ⓓ things

VISIONS BASIC Assessment Program • Copyright © Heinle

Name _____ Date _____

End-of-Book Exam *continued*

➤ **Find the word that best completes the sentence.**

Example: This is a _____.

- Ⓐ dollar
- Ⓑ money
- ⬤ cash register
- Ⓓ cash

21. This is a _____.

- Ⓐ scissors
- Ⓑ wrench
- Ⓒ instrument
- Ⓓ thing

22. This _____ is delicious.

- Ⓐ pizza
- Ⓑ hamburger
- Ⓒ breakfast
- Ⓓ sandwich

23. This _____ has a picture of President Lincoln.

- Ⓐ dollar
- Ⓑ one dollar bill
- Ⓒ five dollar bill
- Ⓓ coin

24. This _____ will cut your hair for fifteen dollars.

- Ⓐ hairstylist
- Ⓑ hairbrush
- Ⓒ artist
- Ⓓ worker

25. This is a _____.

- Ⓐ fork
- Ⓑ knife
- Ⓒ spoon
- Ⓓ dish

➤ **Find the word that best completes the sentence.**

Example: The _____ gives me change.

- ⬤ cashier
- Ⓑ firefighter
- Ⓒ child-care worker
- Ⓓ astronaut

26. I give José a _____ Day card in January.
- Ⓐ New Year's
- Ⓑ Father's
- Ⓒ Valentine's
- Ⓓ Columbus

27. The Valentine's Day card has a big red _____ on it.
- Ⓐ square
- Ⓑ thing
- Ⓒ heart
- Ⓓ parade

28. The steak is more _____ than the hamburger.
- Ⓐ expensive
- Ⓑ thin
- Ⓒ yellow
- Ⓓ fast

29. _____ food is not good for you.
- Ⓐ Healthy
- Ⓑ Unhealthy
- Ⓒ Dishealthy
- Ⓓ Rehealthy

30. Nica's ring is made out of _____.
- Ⓐ fruit
- Ⓑ jewelry
- Ⓒ paint
- Ⓓ gold

Name _____ Date _____

End-of-Book Exam *continued*

C. Grammar (20 points: 2 points each)

➤ **Find the word that best completes the sentence.**

Example: Jean-Claude is _____ than he was last year.
Ⓐ thinner
Ⓑ thin
Ⓒ more thinner
Ⓓ thinnest

31. I think that school is _____ than sports.
Ⓐ important
Ⓑ more important
Ⓒ importanter
Ⓓ more importanter

32. We all have _____ with our lunch.
Ⓐ soups
Ⓑ rices
Ⓒ soup
Ⓓ pea

33. Dana _____ on the soccer team last year.
Ⓐ is
Ⓑ was
Ⓒ were
Ⓓ am

34. Carlos _____ for my grandfather many years ago.
Ⓐ worked
Ⓑ work
Ⓒ works
Ⓓ working

35. I will make a picture and give _____ to Yeny.
Ⓐ them
Ⓑ him
Ⓒ her
Ⓓ it

36. Toby and Sasha _____ not in school yesterday.
Ⓐ are
Ⓑ were
Ⓒ was
Ⓓ isn't

37. The Tigers _____ the Bears in next week's game.
Ⓐ played
Ⓑ will playing
Ⓒ will play
Ⓓ are play

38. My brother _____ us lunch tomorrow.
Ⓐ will make
Ⓑ maked
Ⓒ are making
Ⓓ made

39. Isaac is _____ when he wears his suit and tie.
Ⓐ handsomer
Ⓑ more handsomer
Ⓒ more handsome
Ⓓ most handsomest

40. I like eggs for lunch. Geena likes _____ for breakfast.
Ⓐ them
Ⓑ they
Ⓒ its
Ⓓ she

VISIONS BASIC Assessment Program • Copyright © Heinle

Name _____ Date _____

End-of-Book Exam *continued*

D. Reading (30 points: 2 points each)

<u>Reading 1</u>

Breakfast at Sam's Restaurant

Sasha and Felipe are eating breakfast at Sam's Restaurant. "I want one egg, toast, and bacon," Sasha says. "But I only have two dollars."

"I want an egg, bacon, and juice," Felipe says. "But I have only one dollar and three quarters."

"We need more money," Sasha says.

"I have an idea," Felipe says. "We will get Sam's Combination Breakfast."

"Right!" Sasha says. "We will each eat one egg and one piece of bacon. You will have the juice. I will have the toast."

Felipe smiles. "That will work!" he says. "What a <u>great</u> idea!"

Sam's Restaurant Menu

Egg (1) $1.25

Toast (2) $0.75

Bacon (1) $0.75

Juice (1) $0.70

Sam's Combination Breakfast:
2 eggs, toast, 2 strips of bacon, juice $2.50

➤ **Choose the best answer.**

41. In this story, the word <u>great</u> means _____.
    - Ⓐ very large
    - Ⓑ small
    - Ⓒ very good
    - Ⓓ not good

42. The price of Sam's Combination Breakfast is _____.
    - Ⓐ one dollar and three quarters
    - Ⓑ two dollars
    - Ⓒ two dollars and fifty cents
    - Ⓓ twenty-five cents

43. The problem is that Sasha and Felipe _____.
    - Ⓐ want breakfast
    - Ⓑ need more money
    - Ⓒ need more bacon
    - Ⓓ do not like toast

44. In the end, Sasha and Felipe _____.
    - Ⓐ get one egg
    - Ⓑ each get juice
    - Ⓒ get two Sam's Combination breakfasts
    - Ⓓ get one Sam's Combination Breakfast for two

45. Sasha and Felipe each get _____.
    - Ⓐ toast and eggs
    - Ⓑ the breakfast they want
    - Ⓒ two eggs and bacon
    - Ⓓ toast, juice, eggs, and bacons

Name _____ Date _____

End-of-Book Exam *continued*

Who Is Nelson Mandela?

Nelson Mandela was born in South Africa in 1918. At that time, black and white people did not have equal <u>rights</u> in South Africa.

Mandela worked to give his people their rights. He organized protests. He helped change laws and fight against unfair treatment. But in 1962, Mandela's work put him in <u>prison</u>. In prison, Mandela continued his work. He stayed in prison for 27 years.

By 1990, Mandela's fight for peace was finally successful. South Africa changed. Nelson Mandela got out of prison. The people of South Africa cheered. People around the world cheered. The great man was finally free!

In 1994, Mandela was elected president of South Africa. He also received the Nobel Peace Prize. Mandela was president for five years. He helped people in his country get equal rights. He also helped people in his country get jobs and make money.

In 1999, Mandela left his job as president. South Africa is now a better place than before. Mandela lives and works in South Africa today. He is a great man and a true leader.

© Paul Velasco; Gallo Images/Corbis

Nelson Mandela Timeline

1918: Mandela is born.

1952: Organizes first protests.

1962: Prison.

1962-1990: Continues work in prison.

1993: Nobel Peace Prize.

1994: Elected President.

1999: Steps down as President.

1910 — 2005

VISIONS BASIC Assessment Program • Copyright © Heinle

Name _____ Date _____

End-of-Book Exam *continued*

➤ **Choose the best answer to each question.**

46. The word <u>rights</u> in this story means _____.
Ⓐ not left
Ⓑ correct
Ⓒ goods
Ⓓ things all people can do by law

47. <u>Prison</u> is a place where people _____.
Ⓐ can not get out   Ⓒ can not eat
Ⓑ can not get in   Ⓓ can not laugh

48. From 1952 to 1962, Mandela _____.
Ⓐ was in prison
Ⓑ was president
Ⓒ was free
Ⓓ organized protests

49. Mandela helped _____.
Ⓐ change laws
Ⓑ find a new leader
Ⓒ trade with other countries
Ⓓ change the flag of South Africa

50. Mandela helped people get jobs _____.
Ⓐ before he was president
Ⓑ before he was in prison
Ⓒ when he was in prison
Ⓓ when he was president

51. Which sentence is an opinion?
Ⓐ Mandela was in prison for 27 years.
Ⓑ Mandela was a great president.
Ⓒ Mandela is a leader.
Ⓓ Mandela got the Nobel Peace Prize.

52. Mandela was successful because _____.
Ⓐ he did not have money
Ⓑ he did not give up
Ⓒ he has many friends
Ⓓ he has a nice smile

53. Mandela is known as a great man _____.
Ⓐ only in South Africa
Ⓑ only in Africa
Ⓒ only by black people
Ⓓ by many people around the world

54. Mandela was president when _____.
Ⓐ he was an older man
Ⓑ he was twenty years old
Ⓒ he finished school
Ⓓ he was in prison

55. Mandela worked for freedom _____.
Ⓐ only when he was young
Ⓑ his whole life
Ⓒ only when he got out of prison
Ⓓ because he was in prison

E. Writing (20 points: #56–65, 1 point each; #66, 10 points)

➤ **Write the words that best complete the sentences.**

When I grow up, I will get a job as (**56.**) _____. I will live in the city of (**57.**) _____ in the state of (**58.**) _____. I will live with (**59.**) _____. Every day after work, I will (**60.**) _____. I will also play my favorite sport, (**61.**) _____.

With my money I will buy (**62.**) _____. I will not buy (**63.**) _____. I will eat my favorite food, (**64.**) _____. I will be very (**65.**) _____.

66. What do you eat at a restaurant?

➤ **On a separate piece of paper, write a paragraph. Talk about what you usually buy to eat at a restaurant. How much does each item cost? Are they healthy? What food group does each item belong to?**

Name _____ Date _____

End-of-Book Exam *continued*

Speaking Assessment (100 points: 25 points each)

See Rubric for Speaking Assessment, p. xvi

This Speaking Assessment provides an opportunity to assess students' speaking skills. To administer the test, have the student open to the indicated page in the student book. Ask the questions. The student is graded based on the Rubric for Speaking Assessment on p. xvi of this Assessment Guide.

67. Look at pictures on page 122. Point to the eggs and bacon. What objects do you use to eat this food? Point to the soup. What objects do you use to eat this food? What do you usually eat for dinner? What is your favorite food?

68. Look at the picture on page 136. Point to the dime. How many pennies are in one dime? Point to the twenty dollar bill. Can you buy a car with a twenty dollar bill? What do you buy with your money? Do you pay with cash or with a credit card?

69. Look at the timeline on page 166. On what date is Independence Day? How do people celebrate Independence Day? On what date is Thanksgiving? How do people celebrate Thanksgiving? What is your favorite holiday? How do people celebrate it?

70. Look at the pictures on page 178. Point to the person who is happy. Why do you think this person is happy? When are you happy? Point to the person who is sad. Why do you think this person is sad? When are you sad?

✂ —

Spelling Assessment (100 points: 5 points each)

Each Spelling Assessment provides students with a list of words that test spelling skills. Students are expected to know how to spell both phonetically and by sight and memory. Students should show proficiency in applying spelling rules in appropriate situations. Mastery of vowels, consonants, syllables, silent letters, blends, word endings, patterns, and other fundamental spelling concepts should be demonstrated. To administer the test, read each word on the list and have the student spell it in writing.

1. mad		**11.** families	
2. dish		**12.** price	
3. skate		**13.** writer	
4. dime		**14.** bigger	
5. plate		**15.** will	
6. rice		**16.** pay	
7. then		**17.** happier	
8. speak		**18.** spend	
9. meal		**19.** bill	
10. eggs		**20.** blush	

VISIONS BASIC Assessment Program • Copyright © Heinle

Assessment Answer Key

Diagnostic Test

A. Phonemic Awareness (6 points: 1 point each)
1. C   3. D   5. A
2. C   4. B   6. A

B. Silent Letters (8 points: 2 points each)
7. A   8. A   9. A   10. B

C. Vocabulary (5 points: 1 point each)
11. C   13. B   15. A
12. C   14. C

D. Concepts (4 points: 1 point each)
16. B   17. D   18. B   19. C

E. Letter Recognition (5 points: 1 point each)
20. C   22. D   24. D
21. C   23. C

F. Syllables (3 points: 1 point each)
25. C   26. C   27. D

G. Word Analysis (4 points: 1 point)
28. B   29. A   30. C   31. D

H. Grammar (20 points: 2 points each)
32. C   36. C   40. D
33. A   37. C   41. B
34. D   38. A
35. B   39. C

**I. Writing Conventions: Capitalization
(3 points: 1 point each)**
42. A   43. D   44. D

**J. Writing Conventions: Punctuation
(3 points: 1 point each)**
45. B   46. A   47. C

**K. Writing Conventions: Spelling
(3 points: 1 point each)**
48. D   49. C   50. C

**L. Reading Comprehension
(20 points: 2 points each)**
51. C   55. B   59. B
52. B   56. B   60. D
53. D   57. C
54. C   58. A

**M. The Writing Process (16 points: #61,
1 point; #62, 5 points; #63, 10 points)**
Answers will vary.

Quiz: Chapters A–D

**A. Letters and Sounds: Oral
(20 points: 1 point each)**
1. C   8. B   15. D
2. A   9. D   16. C
3. D   10. C   17. D
4. B   11. A   18. C
5. A   12. B   19. A
6. A   13. A   20. A
7. C   14. B

**B. Letters and Sounds: Written
(20 points: 1 point each)**
21. A   28. D   35. B
22. A   29. A   36. C
23. D   30. A   37. B
24. B   31. A   38. A
25. B   32. D   39. A
26. B   33. B   40. C
27. C   34. B

C. Vocabulary (20 points: 1 point each)
41. B   48. D   55. C
42. D   49. A   56. D
43. A   50. C   57. A
44. C   51. C   58. C
45. C   52. A   59. D
46. B   53. D   60. C
47. C   54. B

**D. Reading (20 points: 1 point each for
61–70; 2 points each for 71–75)**
61. B   66. D   71. D
62. B   67. B   72. A
63. B   68. D   73. C
64. C   69. A   74. D
65. A   70. A   75. B

E. Writing (20 points: 1 point each)
76.–85. Students should be evaluated on the
formation of the letters and words.
86. name
87. Good
88. teacher
89. from
90. sample answer: Mexico
91. classroom
92. sample answer: second
93. flag
94. white
95. floor

Quiz: Chapter 1

A. Listening (20 points: 2 points each)
1. C   5. B   9. B
2. D   6. A   10. A
3. B   7. D
4. A   8. C

B. Vocabulary (20 points: 2 points each)
11. D   15. C   19. A
12. B   16. A   20. C
13. A   17. D
14. B   18. C

C. Grammar (20 points: 2 points each)
21. B   25. B   29. C
22. A   26. B   30. C
23. C   27. A
24. B   28. D

D. Reading (20 points: 5 points each)
31. A   32. B   33. C   34. B

E. Writing (20 points: 2 points each)
35.-44. Answers will vary but should give appropriate information.

Quiz: Chapter 2

A. Listening (20 points: 2 points each)
1. B   5. C   9. A
2. A   6. B   10. C
3. C   7. A
4. D   8. D

B. Vocabulary (20 points: 2 points each)
11. C   15. A   19. D
12. C   16. D   20. A
13. B   17. A
14. B   18. B

C. Grammar (20 points: 2 points each)
21. A   25. C   29. B
22. B   26. B   30. D
23. A   27. D
24. D   28. A

D. Reading (20 points: 5 points each)
31. C   32. B   33. D   34. C

**E. Writing (20 points: #35–44,
    1 point each; #45, 10 points)**
Answers will vary. Sample answers are given.
35. mother   41. thin
36. beautiful   42. brown
37. green   43. medium-length
38. brown   44. curly
39. short   44. *Paragraphs will vary.*
40. tall

Quiz: Chapter 3

A. Listening (20 points: 2 points each)
1. C   5. A   9. B
2. D   6. D   10. C
3. C   7. B
4. C   8. D

B. Vocabulary (20 points: 2 points each)
11. C   15. A   19. A
12. A   16. B   20. D
13. B   17. A
14. D   18. C

C. Grammar (20 points: 2 points each)
21. B   25. D   29. A
22. B   26. A   30. C
23. A   27. C
24. C   28. B

D. Reading (20 points: 5 points each)
31. A   32. D   33. C   34. C

**E. Writing (20 points: #35–44,
    1 point each; #45, 10 points)**
Answers will vary. Sample answers are given.
35. baseball   41. my sister
36. my friends   42. after school
37. usually   43. the drums
38. after school   44. never
39. a bat   45. *Paragraphs will vary.*
40. salsa

Quiz: Chapter 4

A. Listening (20 points: 2 points each)
1. B   5. C   9. C
2. D   6. D   10. B
3. B   7. A
4. A   8. B

B. Vocabulary (20 points: 2 points each)
11. A   15. C   19. D
12. D   16. B   20. C
13. B   17. C
14. A   18. A

C. Grammar (20 points: 2 points each)
21. A   25. B   29. A
22. B   26. B   30. B
23. B   27. A
24. A   28. B

D. Reading (20 points: 5 points each)
31. B   32. A   33. A   34. D

**E. Writing (20 points: #35–44,
    1 point each; #45, 10 points)**
Answers will vary. Sample answers are given.
35. apartment/house   41. music
36. the living room   42. paint
37. is   43. read
38. bed   44. sleep
39. are   45. *Paragraphs will vary.*
40. bookcases

Quiz: Chapter 5

A. Listening (20 points: 2 points each)
1. B   5. C   9. A
2. B   6. B   10. B
3. B   7. D
4. A   8. C

B. Vocabulary (20 points: 2 points each)
11. C   15. A   19. B
12. B   16. B   20. D
13. C   17. A
14. D   18. D

C. Grammar (20 points: 2 points each)
21. D   25. C   29. B
22. A   26. B   30. C
23. D   27. D
24. B   28. C

D. Reading (20 points: 5 points each)
31. D   32. A   33. D   34. A

VISIONS BASIC TAssessment Guide   • Copyright © Heinle

**E. Writing (20 points: #35–44,
1 point each; #45, 10 points)**

Answers will vary. Sample answers are given.

35. school
36. walk
37. take the bus
38. walk
39. 7:30
40. 8:00

41. 3:30
42. 3:15
43. the newspaper
44. walk in the park
45. *Paragraphs will vary.*

Mid-Book Exam Chapters 1–5

A. Listening (10 points: 1 point each)

1. B
2. A
3. D
4. D

5. D
6. B
7. D
8. A

9. A
10. B

B. Vocabulary (20 points: 2 points each)

11. C
12. B
13. D
14. C
15. A

16. B
17. B
18. A
19. D
20. B

21. D
22. B
23. C
24. A
25. B

26. D
27. C
28. D
29. A
30. C

C. Grammar (20 points: 2 points each)

31. A
32. D
33. B
34. A

35. B
36. A
37. B
38. A

39. C
40. A

D. Reading (30 points: 2 points each)

41. B
42. C
43. D
44. A
45. B

46. A
47. B
48. A
49. D
50. C

51. B
52. C
53. C
54. D
55. A

**E. Writing (20 points: #56–65,
1 point each; #66, 10 points)**

Answers will vary. Sample answers are given.

56. Houston, Texas
57. in a house
58. parents and sister
59. Lincoln Middle School
60. reading
61. math
62. gym
63. Pete
64. play music
65. soccer
66. *Paragraphs will vary.*

Quiz: Chapter 6

A. Listening (20 points: 2 points each)

1. D
2. A
3. C
4. B

5. A
6. C
7. C
8. B

9. B
10. B

B. Vocabulary (20 points: 2 points each)

11. D
12. B
13. A
14. C

15. B
16. B
17. C
18. A

19. C
20. A

C. Grammar (20 points: 2 points each)

21. D
22. A
23. A
24. A

25. B
26. D
27. A
28. D

29. C
30. B

D. Reading (20 points: 5 points each)

31. C
32. B
33. D
34. A

**E. Writing (20 points: #35–44,
1 point each; #45, 10 points)**

Answers will vary. Sample answers are given.

35. toast
36. eggs
37. juice
38. a sandwich
39. milk
40. salad

41. fish
42. potatoes
43. peas
44. pizza
45. *Paragraphs will vary.*

Quiz: Chapter 7

A. Listening (20 points: 2 points each)

1. A
2. B
3. C
4. B

5. A
6. C
7. B
8. B

9. B
10. D

B. Vocabulary (20 points: 2 points each)

11. B
12. A
13. C
14. A

15. B
16. B
17. A
18. B

19. A
20. C

C. Grammar (20 points: 2 points each)

21. D
22. B
23. A
24. C

25. C
26. B
27. A
28. B

29. A
30. A

D. Reading (20 points: 5 points each)

31. B
32. A
33. A
34. C

**E. Writing (20 points: #35–44,
1 point each; #45, 10 points)**

Answers will vary. Sample answers are given.

35. pay
36. cash
37. write
38. check
39. credit card
40. ATM card

41. price
42. Expensive
43. cheap
44. clothes
45. *Paragraphs will vary.*

Quiz: Chapter 8

A. Listening (20 points: 2 points each)

1. A
2. B
3. A
4. B

5. A
6. A
7. D
8. B

9. A
10. A

B. Vocabulary (20 points: 2 points each)

11. D
12. B
13. A
14. C

15. C
16. B
17. A
18. C

19. D
20. B

C. Grammar (20 points: 2 points each)

21. C	25. D	29. A
22. A	26. D	30. B
23. D	27. C	
24. A	28. B	

D. Reading (20 points: 5 points each)

31. A	32. B	33. D	34. A

**E. Writing (20 points: #35–44,
    1 point each; #45, 10 points)**

Answers will vary. Sample answers are given.

35. mother	41. carpenter
36. an artist	42. firefighter
37. father	43. chef
38. a waiter	44. cashier
39. a mechanic	45. *Paragraphs will vary.*
40. doctor	

Quiz: Chapter 9

A. Listening (20 points: 2 points each)

1. B	5. D	9. B
2. A	6. C	10. A
3. B	7. B	
4. A	8. A	

B. Vocabulary (20 points: 2 points each)

11. C	15. B	19. B
12. C	16. B	20. D
13. D	17. D	
14. D	18. A	

C. Grammar (20 points: 2 points each)

21. C	25. C	29. C
22. D	26. B	30. A
23. A	27. D	
24. B	28. A	

D. Reading (20 points: 5 points each)

31. D	32. C	33. C	34. D

**E. Writing (20 points: #35–44,
    1 point each; #45, 10 points)**

Answers will vary. Sample answers are given.

35. New Year's Day
36. Valentine's Day
37. President's Day
38. Mother's Day
39. Father's Day
40. Independence Day
41. the fireworks
42. Halloween
43. Thanksgiving
44. I like turkey
45. *Paragraphs will vary.*

Quiz: Chapter 10

A. Listening (20 points: 2 points each)

1. B	5. D	9. C
2. D	6. C	10. B
3. B	7. B	
4. C	8. A	

B. Vocabulary (20 points: 2 points each)

11. D	15. B	19. A
12. D	16. B	20. B
13. A	17. A	
14. B	18. D	

C. Grammar (20 points: 2 points each)

21. B	25. B	29. C
22. A	26. B	30. C
23. B	27. A	
24. D	28. D	

D. Reading (20 points: 5 points each)

31. C	32. B	33. D	34. B

**E. Writing (20 points: #35–44,
    1 point each; #45, 10 points)**

Answers will vary. Sample answers are given.

35. excited	41. laughed
36. *name will vary*	42. sad
37. bored	43. cry
38. yawned	44. happy
39. doctor	45. *Paragraphs will vary.*
40. shy	

End-of-Book Exam: Chapters 6–10

A. Listening (10 points: 1 point each)

1. B	5. D	9. A
2. D	6. A	10. C
3. A	7. B	
4. B	8. A	

B. Vocabulary (20 points: 1 point each)

11 C	16. C	21. B	26. A
12. C	17. A	22. A	27. C
13. B	18. C	23. C	28. A
14. C	19. D	24. A	29. B
15. A	20. C	25. C	30. D

C. Grammar (20 points: 2 points each)

31. B	35. D	39. C
32. C	36. B	40. A
33. B	37. C	
34. A	38. A	

D. Reading (30 points: 2 points each)

41. C	46. D	51. B
42. C	47. A	52. B
43. B	48. D	53. D
44. D	49. A	54. A
45. B	50. D	55. B

**E. Writing (20 points: #56–65, 1 point each;
    #66, 10 points)**

Answers will vary. Sample answers are given.

56. a firefighter	62. a computer
57. Atlanta	63. a car
58. Georgia	64. fish
59. my family	65. happy
60. go to the park	66. *Paragraphs will vary.*
61. baseball	

VISIONS BASIC Assessment Guide • Copyright © Heinle

Name _____ Date _____

Student Self-Assessment

Part I: Circle the number that best describes you.

A. How I feel about my work in English:	Unhappy	1	2	3	4	Happy
B. My speaking and listening are:	Not Improving	1	2	3	4	Improving
C. My reading is:	Not Improving	1	2	3	4	Improving
D. My writing is:	Not Improving	1	2	3	4	Improving
E. My work is:	Too Hard	1	2	3	4	Too Easy
F. My work is:	Not Interesting	1	2	3	4	Very Interesting

Part II: Complete these sentences.

A. The best thing that I did/learned lately is _____

_____

B. I would like to learn _____

_____

C. I am best at _____

_____

D. I need some help with _____

_____

E. My learning and practicing plans are to _____

_____

VISIONS BASIC Student Resource

Editor's Checklist

I. Ideas	✓	comments
A. Is the purpose of my writing clear?	____	
B. Do I stay focused on the topic?	____	
C. Do I support my ideas with details, facts, and examples?	____	

II. Organization	✓	comments
A. Is my writing clear and logical?	____	
B. Are my ideas tied together?	____	

III. Voice	✓	comments
A. Do I give my own ideas and opinions?	____	
B. Do I write for a specific audience?	____	

IV. Sentence Fluency	✓	comments
A. Are my sentences complete? Do they have a subject and a verb?	____	
B. Did I use different types and styles of sentences?	____	

V. Word Choice	✓	comments
A. Do I use vivid and exact words?	____	
B. Did I use a reference aid to choose better words?	____	

VI. Writing Conventions	✓	comments
Grammar and Usage		
A. Is my writing in the correct tense (for example, present or past)	____	
B. Did I use subject and object pronouns correctly	____	
C. Did I use the pronouns *she*, *her*, or *hers* for a woman or a girl, and *he*, *him*, or *his* for a man or a boy?	____	
D. Do my verbs agree with their subjects? (I *go*/she *goes*)	____	
Spelling		
E. Did I check the spelling of all words I'm not sure about?	____	
F. Did I use spell check if I wrote my paper on a computer?	____	
Capitalization		
G. Does each sentence start with a capital letter?	____	
H. Do I capitalize proper nouns?	____	
Punctuation		
I. Do I punctuate each sentence with the right mark (?!)?	____	
J. Do I put quotation marks (" ") around any direct speech?	____	
K. Do I use apostrophes (') in contractions and possessives?	____	

VII. Presentation	✓	comments
A. Is my name, the date, and a title on the page?	____	
B. Did I indent the first line of each paragraph?	____	
C. Did I use my best handwriting? OR Did I create an attractive computer presentation?	____	

VISIONS BASIC Assessment Program • Copyright © Heinle

Writer's name _____ Editor's name _____

Peer Editing Checklist

Use this checklist to edit your peer's writing.
You may also use it to check your own writing.

1. Is there a title? _____ Yes _____ No

2. Is the first sentence of each paragraph indented? _____ Yes _____ No

3. Does each sentence start with a capital letter? _____ Yes _____ No

4. Does each sentence end with a punctuation mark? _____ Yes _____ No

5. Does each name start with a capital letter? _____ Yes _____ No

6. Write one correct sentence from the paper.

_____

7. Write one sentence that has a mistake.

_____

8. Rewrite the sentence correctly.

_____

Use these editing symbols:

¶	Start a new paragraph.
∧	Insert a word or words.
sp	Correct a spelling error.
CAP	Use a capital letter.
lc	Use a lowercase letter.
p	Correct a punctuation error.
exact	Use a more exact word.
?	What does this mean?
～	Transpose these letters or words.

Portfolio: Activity Rating and Reflection Sheet

Part I: Rating

Write the name of each activity in your work folder on the left. Think about how much you liked it. Circle one number for each activity.

Chapter _____ Activities	I didn't like it.	I liked it a little.	I liked it.	I liked it very much.
_____	1	2	3	4
_____	1	2	3	4
_____	1	2	3	4
_____	1	2	3	4
_____	1	2	3	4
_____	1	2	3	4
_____	1	2	3	4
_____	1	2	3	4

Part II: Reflection

1. My Portfolio choice for Chapter _____

I chose to put _____ in my Portfolio

because _____.

2. How I Learned

I learned best from...

_____ listening and speaking.   _____ reading.   _____ writing.

I liked working...

_____ by myself.   _____ with a partner.   _____ with a small group.

_____ with the whole class.

VISIONS BASIC Assessment Program • Copyright © Heinle

VISIONS BASIC Assessment Program • Copyright © Heinle

Name _____   Date _____

Word Study and Spelling

Keep a list of new words that you learn.

Use a dictionary, a glossary, the Newbury House Dictionary CD-ROM, or an online dictionary to find definition.

Word	Page	Sentence from Textbook	Definition	Your Sentence

83

Name _____ Date _____

Word Study and Spelling Assessment Chart

1. Exchange your *Word Study and Spelling* pages with a partner.
2. Choose five words and ask your partner to spell them on a piece of paper.
3. Choose another five words and ask your partner to write a sentence using each.
4. Check your partner's work.
5. Record the number of words spelled correctly in the first row of your partner's chart.
6. Record the number of words used correctly in a sentence in the second row.
7. Record the words that were spelled or used incorrectly in the third row.

My Score	Chapter 1	Chapter 2	Chapter 3	Chapter 4	Chapter 5	Chapter 6	Chapter 7	Chapter 8	Chapter 9	Chapter 10
How many words did I spell correctly?	Correct: Incorrect:	Correct: Incorrect:	Correct: Incorrect:	Correct: Incorrect:	Correct: Incorrect:	Correct: Incorrect:	Correct: Incorrect:	Correct: Incorrect:	Correct: Incorrect:	Correct: Incorrect:
How many words did I use in a sentence correctly?	Correct: Incorrect:	Correct: Incorrect:	Correct: Incorrect:	Correct: Incorrect:	Correct: Incorrect:	Correct: Incorrect:	Correct: Incorrect:	Correct: Incorrect:	Correct: Incorrect:	Correct: Incorrect:
Which words do I need to study?										

VISIONS BASIC Assessment Program • Copyright © Heinle

Name _____ Date _____

Speaker _____ Topic _____

Active Listening Checklist

Use this checklist to evaluate how well you listen and understand.

1. I liked _____ because _____

_____

2. I want to know more about _____

_____

3. I thought the presentation was interesting. _____ Yes _____ No

4. The speaker stayed on the topic. _____ Yes _____ No

5. I did not understand _____

_____

6. I needed the speaker to repeat or clarify _____

_____

My own criteria:

7. _____

_____

8. _____

_____

9. _____

_____

Name _____ Date _____

Topic _____

Speaking Checklist

Use this checklist to evaluate your speaking.

1. Did I speak too slowly, too quickly, or just right? _____ Yes _____ No

2. Was the tone of my voice too high, too low, or just right? _____ Yes _____ No

3. Did I speak loudly enough for the audience to hear me? _____ Yes _____ No

4. Did I produce the correct intonation patterns of sentences? _____ Yes _____ No

5. Did I have a good opening? _____ Yes _____ No

6. Did I look at my audience? _____ Yes _____ No

7. Did I speak with feeling? _____ Yes _____ No

8. Did I support my ideas with facts and examples? _____ Yes _____ No

9. Did I tell the audience how I feel about the topic? _____ Yes _____ No

10. Did I use interesting, specific words? _____ Yes _____ No

11. Did I use visuals to make the speech interesting? _____ Yes _____ No

My own criteria:

12. _____ _____ Yes _____ No

13. _____ _____ Yes _____ No

14. _____ _____ Yes _____ No

Name _____ Date _____

Title of Reading Selection _____

Reading Checklist

Use this checklist to evaluate your reading.

1. Why did I read this selection? _____

_____

2. I set a goal for how much I wanted to read. _____ Yes _____ No

3. I used the pictures to help me understand. _____ Yes _____ No

4. I used graphic features to help me understand. _____ Yes _____ No

5. I used word parts to help me understand words. _____ Yes _____ No

6. I used context to help me understand words. _____ Yes _____ No

7. I looked up words that I didn't know in a dictionary, glossary, thesaurus, or CD-ROM or online dictionary. _____ Yes _____ No

8. I adjusted my reading rate to my purpose. _____ Yes _____ No

9. I used what I already know to help me understand. _____ Yes _____ No

10. I can summarize the selection. _____ Yes _____ No

11. The main idea of the selection is _____

_____

12. I learned _____

_____

My own criteria:

13. _____

14. _____

Name _____ Date _____

Text/Presentation_____

Viewing Checklist

Visuals (photographs, pictures, maps, charts) help you understand texts and presentations better. Analyzing visuals for their usefulness will help you to learn how to create good visuals.

Think about these points as you view and create visuals.

1. Do I understand the purpose of this visual?   _____ Yes   _____ No

2. What is the purpose? _____

   _____

3. Does this visual help me to understand better?   _____ Yes   _____ No

4. How does it help me understand? _____

   _____

5. Is the visual labeled clearly?   _____ Yes   _____ No

6. Does the visual give me extra information?   _____ Yes   _____ No

7. What did I learn from the visual? _____

   _____

8. Would I create the same visual for this text/presentation?   _____ Yes   _____ No

9. What would I do differently? _____

   _____

My own criteria:

10. _____

11. _____

VISIONS BASIC Assessment Program • Copyright © Heinle